GCS
Sc

First published 1998

Letts Educational
Schools and Colleges Division
9–15 Aldine Street
London W12 8AW
Tel 0181 740 2270
Fax 0181 740 2280

Editorial, design and production by Moondisks Ltd, Cambridge

British Library Cataloguing-in-Publication Data
A CIP record for this book is available from the British Library.

ISBN 1 84085 146 5

Printed and bound in Great Britain

Letts Educational is the trading name of BPP (Letts Educational) Ltd.

Contents

Introduction

This Letts GCSE Science Dictionary has been specially written for all of the new GCSE syllabuses and is suitable for both Foundation and Higher tiers. It is closely linked to the National Curriculum and will help you to master the key concepts in Key Stage 4 Science, and to refresh your memory of the important topics from Key Stage 3.

The dictionary will help you with your Double Science course or Single Science courses. During your work in Science you will come across terms, ideas and definitions that you have not met before and also those you have met, but forgotten. This book will help you with your learning, providing a quick source of information for new topics or 'reminders' for revision purposes.

The entries are arranged alphabetically. Where appropriate, illustrations are used to assist you with your research. Many of the illustrations are taken from companion Letts GCSE Science or individual GCSE Single Science texts.

Text highlighted in blue indicates cross-referencing. If you are not sure that you have a sound understanding of the highlighted word you can turn to it in the dictionary to check. In this way you should develop a fuller understanding of the term, idea or definition under review.

We hope that this book will help you to progress in GCSE Science or in your GCSE Single Sciences. The dictionary has been written by experienced examiners and teachers, very much with exam success in mind. But as well as helping you to achieve your desired grade, we hope that this book will give you an insight into and an enjoyment of Science, which is vital to an understanding of the modern world.

absolute temperature There is a minimum temperature below which it will never be possible to cool anything. This is called absolute zero and is −273 °C. This is the starting point for the Kelvin temperature scale. On this scale 0 °C is 273 K and 100 °C is 373 K.

absorber An absorber does not reflect or transmit particles or radiation that hit it. Aluminium foil is an absorber of alpha particles. A dark, dull surface is an absorber of infra-red radiation.

absorption Absorption is the term used to describe the movement of materials across a surface into a cell, tissue or organ. Movement occurs by simple diffusion or active transport. Surfaces that are adapted for absorption usually have a large surface area that is thin, moist and permeable to the substances being absorbed. Examples of where absorption occurs include the lining of the gut, in particular in the ileum, the alveoli of the lungs and the root hair cells of plants.

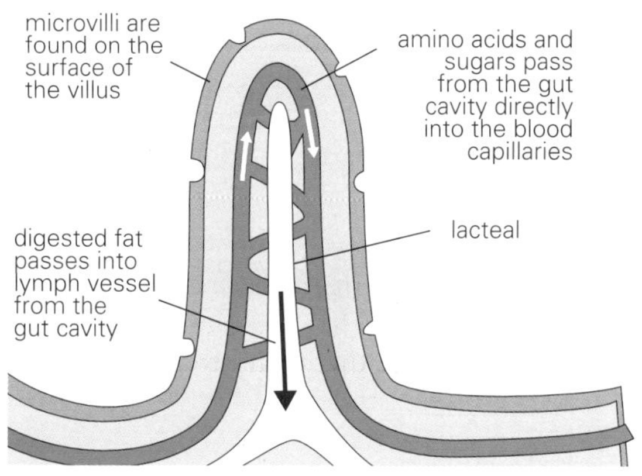

Absorption of food molecules through a villus

acceleration An acceleration is a change in velocity. It can be a change in speed, a change in direction or both.
Acceleration is defined as *increase in velocity ÷ time taken* and is measured in m/s^2. A negative acceleration is called a deceleration.

accommodation The shape of the lens of the eye and its pupil size have to be changed in order to focus the eye on near or distant objects. When muscles present in the ciliary body contract, the ligaments suspending the lens slacken. The lens then becomes more convex, bending the light more and is therefore more effective at focusing light from nearer objects. When these muscles relax the converse occurs. This process is called accommodation.

accuracy Accuracy is a term that refers to the properties of a measuring instrument. The manufacturer usually specifies the accuracy as a percentage. If a voltmeter has an accuracy of 10% this means that a reading of 2.0 V represents a voltage of 2.0 V ± 0.2 V.

acid A substance that dissolves in water to form a solution with a pH below 7. An acid contains hydrogen which can be replaced by a metal to form a salt. When an acid dissolves in water $H^+(aq)$ ions are formed. A strong acid completely ionises in water and a weak acid only partly ionises. Common strong acids include hydrochloric acid, HCl, sulphuric acid, H_2SO_4, and nitric acid, HNO_3. A common weak acid is ethanoic acid, CH_3COOH.

acid rain Sulphur and nitrogen oxides are produced from the burning of fossil fuels. When they escape into the atmosphere, they form sulphuric and nitric acids. These can have effects on the environment, e.g. erode stonework, lower the pH of lakes and rivers killing wildlife, and cause damage to trees.

activation energy This is the energy required to start a reaction. It is shown in the energy level diagram. A catalyst lowers the activation energy. More particles achieve this lower energy and so the reaction is faster.

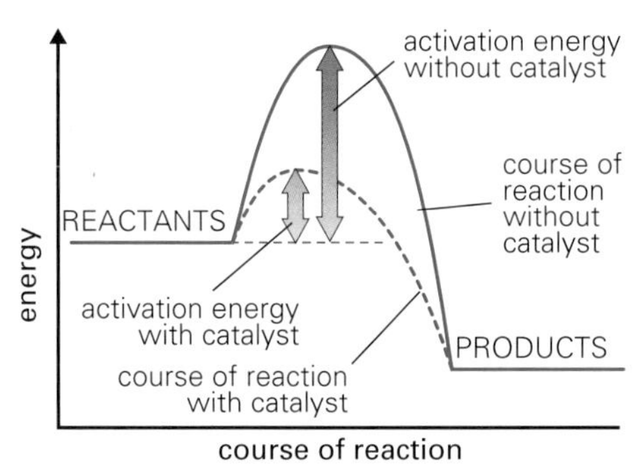

Effect of a catalyst on the activation energy

active site Enzymes are large protein molecules. Not all of the enzyme takes part in an interaction with its substrate. The particular area where interaction takes place is called the active site.

active transport Active transport is a process which enables the movement of particles across a membrane, often against a concentration gradient. It requires energy and this is provided by respiration. One example where this occurs is in the uptake of mineral ions by plant roots.

addition reaction A reaction where two substances react to form a single product, e.g.

ethene + hydrogen → ethane

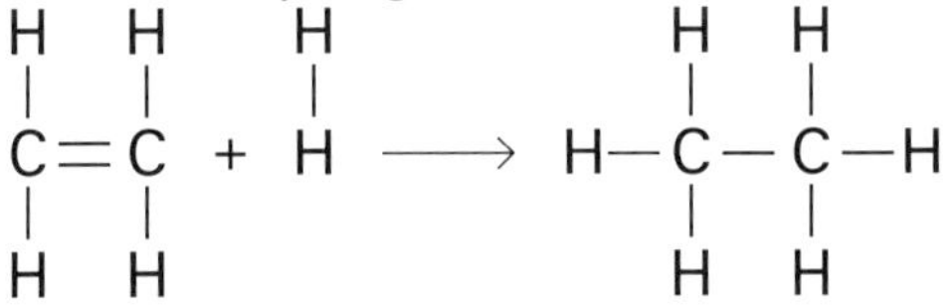

$$\begin{array}{ccccccccccc}
\mathrm{H} & & \mathrm{H} & & \mathrm{H} & & & \mathrm{H} & & \mathrm{H} & \\
\vert & & \vert & & \vert & & & \vert & & \vert & \\
\mathrm{C} & = & \mathrm{C} & + & \mathrm{H} & \longrightarrow & \mathrm{H}- & \mathrm{C} & - & \mathrm{C} & -\mathrm{H} \\
\vert & & \vert & & & & & \vert & & \vert & \\
\mathrm{H} & & \mathrm{H} & & & & & \mathrm{H} & & \mathrm{H} &
\end{array}$$

The opposite of an addition reaction is an elimination reaction.

adenosine triphosphate (ATP) Adenosine triphosphate is produced during respiration and photosynthesis. It is a compound that provides a means to store energy or transfer it to compounds taking part in reactions in a cell. Compounds that are phosphorylated are more reactive.

aerobic respiration Plants and animals need a supply of energy in order to function. They obtain energy from their food by oxidising it, forming carbon dioxide and water as wastes. This process is known as aerobic respiration. Glucose is the most common substrate for this process but cells can oxidise fats and proteins.

glucose + oxygen → carbon dioxide + water + energy

Some of the energy is released as heat but most is used to make ATP. Aerobic respiration takes place inside a cell in structures known as mitochondria.

Examples of the way plants and animals use energy include: getting muscles to contract; getting neurones to transmit nerve impulses; and enabling active transport to take place.

air Air is a mixture of gases. As a mixture its composition will vary. Typical composition is approximately one fifth oxygen and four fifths nitrogen with small amounts of argon (and the other noble gases), carbon dioxide and water vapour. Hydrogen is not normally present in air. The composition of air is kept approximately constant by process of combustion, respiration and corrosion that use up oxygen and photosynthesis of green plants that produces oxygen. Over millions of years the composition of the air has changed.

air resistance This is a force that acts on any object moving through the air. It acts in the direction opposite to the motion. The faster the speed of the object, the greater the size of the air resistance force acting on it.

alcohol The name alcohol refers to a family of organic compounds each containing an –OH group. The simplest members of the family are methanol, CH_3OH, and ethanol, C_2H_5OH. The simplest members are miscible with water. The name alcohol is commonly used for ethanol. This is present in alcoholic drinks. It can be produced by fermentation of sugar solutions using enzymes in yeast. Alternatively it can be produced by the reaction of ethene with steam (an addition reaction)

$$C_2H_4 + H_2O \rightarrow C_2H_5OH.$$

alimentary canal The alimentary canal (or gut) is an organ system whose function is to treat the food ingested by a mammal. It is a tubular structure that is modified along its length to carry out the processes of digestion and absorption. Different regions of the alimentary canal carry out different specific functions. Each region shows specific features that make it efficient for a particular role.

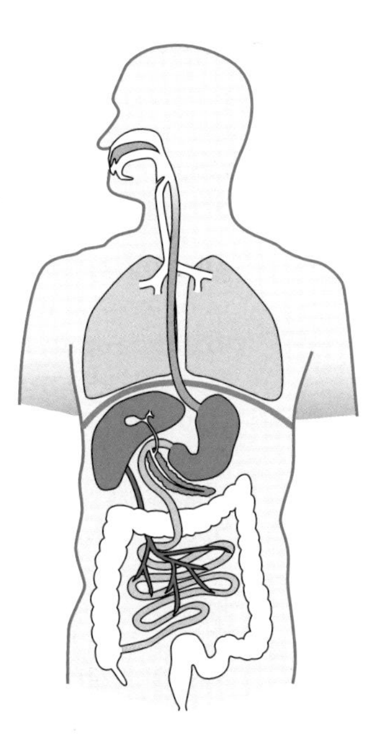

The human alimentary canal and associated organs

alkali An alkali is a metal oxide or hydroxide (base) that dissolves in water to form a solution with a pH greater than 7. An alkali is neutralised by an acid to form a salt and water. Common alkalis include sodium hydroxide, NaOH, potassium hydroxide, KOH, calcium hydroxide, $Ca(OH)_2$ and ammonium hydroxide, NH_4OH.

alkali metal An element in group I of the Periodic Table (see p. 76). These metals, lithium, Li, sodium, Na, potassium, K, rubidium, Rb and caesium, Cs, increase in reactivity down the group. For example in the reaction of alkali metals with water to produce the metal hydroxide and hydrogen, the difference in reactivity can be seen. Atoms of these elements all contain a single electron in the outer energy level (shell).

alkaline-earth metal These are elements in group 2 of the Periodic Table (see p. 76). They include magnesium, Mg, calcium, Ca and barium, Ba. The reactivity increases down the group.

alkane A family of hydrocarbons with a general formula of C_nH_{2n+2}. The simplest alkane is methane, CH_4, the main constituent of natural gas. All of the alkanes are saturated compounds containing only single covalent bonds. Petroleum (crude oil) is a mixture of alkanes. The lowest members of the family, methane, ethane, propane and butane, are gases. Other members, e.g. hexane and octane, are liquids and the higher members are waxy solids. Alkanes have few reactions apart from combustion. They burn in a plentiful supply of air or oxygen to form carbon dioxide and water. In a limited supply of oxygen, carbon monoxide and water are produced. Carbon monoxide is poisonous.

alkene A family of hydrocarbons with a general formula of C_nH_{2n}. The simplest alkene is ethene, C_2H_4. Alkenes contain a double covalent bond. They take part in addition reactions, e.g. ethene and bromine.

```
H   H    Br              H   H
|   |    |               |   |
C = C  + Br  ——→   Br — C — C — Br
|   |                    |   |
H   H                    H   H
```

allele Genes may exist in more than one form. Each form is known as an allele.

allotropy When an element can exist in two or more forms in the same physical state, it is said to show allotropy. The different forms are called allotropes. Diamond and graphite are two allotropes of carbon. Different allotropes exist because of different arrangements of atoms. Other elements showing allotropy include sulphur, phosphorus, tin and oxygen.

alloy An alloy is a metal made by mixing two or more metals together, e.g. brass is a mixture of copper and zinc. The alloy has different properties than the pure metals. For example, duralumin (an alloy of aluminium) is stronger than pure aluminium and more suitable for aircraft construction. Solder is an alloy of tin and lead with a lower melting point than either pure metal, making it more suitable for joining two metals together by soldering. The most widely used alloy is steel where iron is mixed, not with a metal, but with small amounts of carbon. Forming an alloy alters the structure of the metal.

alpha particle An alpha particle is one type of radioactive emission given out when an unstable nucleus that has more than 82 protons changes to a more stable form. An alpha particle consists of two protons and two neutrons and is sometimes referred to as a helium nucleus.

alternating current An alternating current is one that changes direction. The current from the mains supply is alternating, it changes direction 100 times each second. Cycle dynamos also generate alternating current.

amalgam Many metals form alloys when mixed with mercury. These alloys are called amalgams. They are used for fillings in teeth.

amino acid A molecule containing both $-COOH$ and $-NH_2$ groups. Amino acids link together in chains to form proteins. The links are called 'peptide links'.

```
     COOH
      |
  H — C — NH2
      |
      R
```

an amino acid

R represents any group

ammeter An ammeter is a device that measures the size of an electric current. It is always placed in series with the current that it is measuring.

ammonia Ammonia is a colourless gas which turns red litmus blue. It has a formula NH_3. It is manufactured from nitrogen and hydrogen in the Haber process. It is used for making fertilisers, e.g. ammonium sulphate, and for making other chemicals, e.g. nitric acid.

amp The amp is the unit of electric current. A current of one amp passes when charge flows at the rate of one coulomb per second.

amplitude The amplitude of a wave motion is the maximum displacement from the mean position. The diagram shows the distance that is the amplitude of a wave.

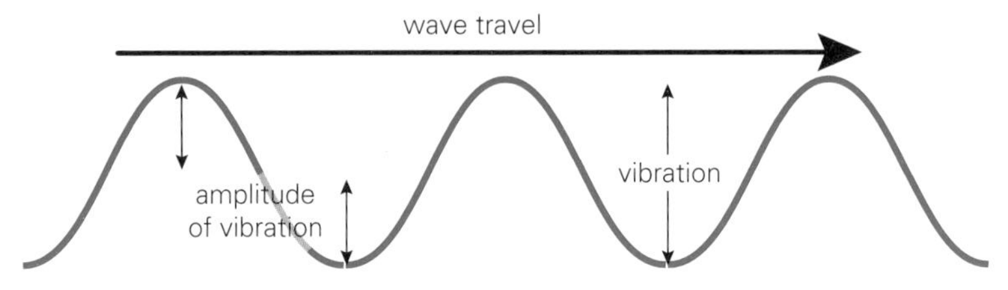

Vibrations of a transverse wave

anaerobic respiration Anaerobic respiration is the release of energy from a food molecule, such as glucose, in the absence of oxygen. This type of respiration occurs in both plants and animals, and micro-organisms (e.g. yeast), but the products differ. Anaerobic respiration is summarised by the following equations.

animal cells: glucose → lactic acid + energy

plant cells: glucose → ethanol + carbon dioxide + energy

Anaerobic respiration releases much less energy per molecule of glucose than aerobic respiration. Anaerobically respiring yeast cells are employed in fermentation to produce alcoholic drinks.

analysis Finding out the elements present in a substance is called qualitative analysis. Quantitative analysis is finding out how much of each element is present.

angle of incidence When light meets a boundary between two materials, the angle of incidence is the angle between the direction of the incident light and a line drawn at right angles to the boundary (called the normal line).

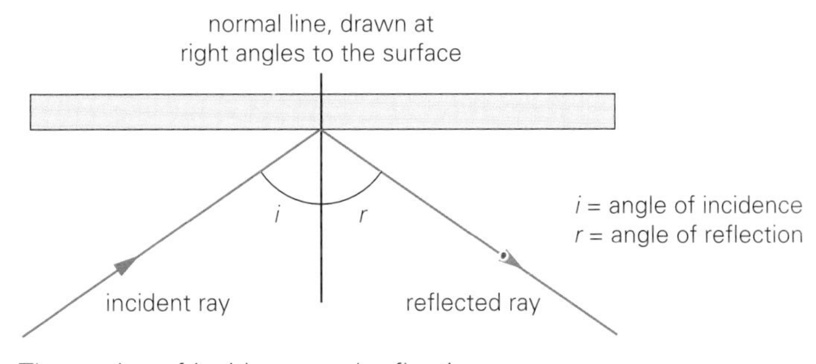

The angles of incidence and reflection

angle of reflection When light is reflected at a boundary between two materials, the angle of reflection is the angle between the direction of the reflected light and a line drawn at right angles to the boundary (called the normal line).

angle of refraction When light crosses a boundary between two materials, the angle of refraction is the angle between the normal line and the direction of travel in the material it has passed into.

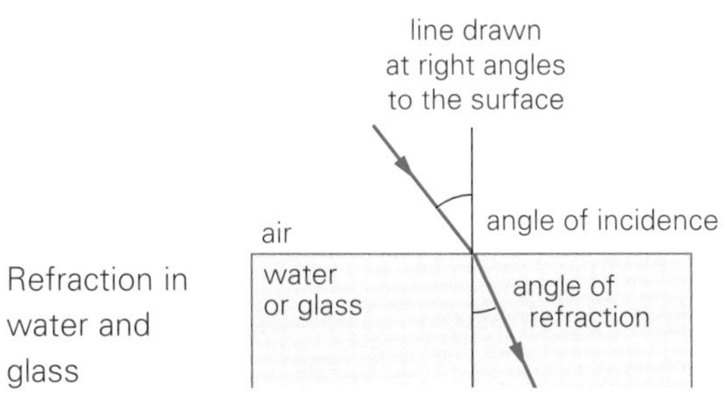

Refraction in water and glass

anion A negatively charged ion, e.g. chloride, Cl^-, hydroxide, OH^- or oxide, O^{2-}. Anions are attracted to the positively charged electrode (anode) during electrolysis.

anode The positively charged electrode in electrolysis. At the anode there is a shortage of electrons. Negatively charged ions (anions) are discharged and give up electrons to the anode, e.g. $2Cl^- \rightarrow Cl_2 + 2e^-$.

anodising The method of finishing aluminium involving the thickening of the oxide coating by electrolysis. The aluminium object to be anodised is made the anode in an electrolysis cell. Oxide produced at the anode produces an oxide coating. This oxide coating can be dyed to give the aluminium object a colour.

anorexia nervosa An eating disorder where a person has minimal intake of food over prolonged periods of time. It can lead to massive weight loss and, eventually, death.

antagonistic pair A muscle can 'do work' only when it contracts. Relaxation of a contracted muscle will not necessarily reverse the change it brought about on contracting. Muscles are often found in pairs, having opposite effects. The two muscles that work as a pair, each reversing the action of the other, are known as an antagonistic pair. Examples include the circular and longitudinal muscles of the alimentary canal wall, the circular and radial muscles of the iris of the eye and the biceps and triceps.

antibiotic Antibiotics are substances, made by living organisms, that are selectively toxic. Some are used medicinally. They work by preventing the growth of pathogens. Examples of antibiotics include penicillin G, amphotericin B and actinomycin D. Antibiotics are ineffective against viruses.

antibodies Antibodies are proteins that help to neutralise the effect of antigens. They are produced by white blood cells called lymphocytes. Each antibody is highly specific in its action, interacting with one antigen only.

antigens Foreign cells which enter the human body have antigenic molecules on their surface membranes. Antigenic molecules act as markers or signals and are recognised as 'non-self' by the body. The body responds by forming antibodies specific to the antigens it has recognised.

antiseptic This is a substance used to prevent micro-organisms reproducing. It can only be used outside the human body.

antitoxins Antitoxins are substances produced by lymphocytes to neutralise poisonous compounds (toxins) produced by pathogens.

aorta The aorta is the main artery of the body that carries blood away from the left ventricle of the heart. The wall of the aorta is extremely well-endowed with elastic tissue, including muscle. Its structure enables it to withstand the enormous pressure exerted by the left ventricular contraction. Elastic recoil occurs when the aorta returns to its unstretched diameter as the ventricle relaxes. This helps to maintain continuous blood flow through the aorta and the rest of the systemic circuit by 'smoothing out' the sudden surges of pressure.

armature The armature is the moving part of an electromagnetic device. In a motor, the armature consists of the coil and its core. In a relay and a bell, the armature is a piece of soft iron that is attracted to the electromagnet.

artery Blood travels away from the heart to organs, tissues and cells in blood vessels called arteries. Compared to veins, arteries have relatively thicker walls, more elastic tissue including muscle, a smaller lumen (bore) and no valves.

artificial insemination (AI) This is a technique involving the injection of sperm into a female by artificial means, e.g. by syringe. It is commonly used in the breeding of cattle.

asexual Asexual means without involving sex. Plants, simple animals and micro-organisms can reproduce asexually. Examples of asexual reproduction include binary fission in protozoans (single celled animals) and the involvement of structures such as bulbs, corms and tubers in higher plants.

atom The smallest particle of an element which can exist.

atomic number The number of protons in the nucleus of an atom. It is equal to the number of electrons orbiting the nucleus in the atom.

ATP (See **adenosine triphosphate**.)

attract When two objects pull together they attract each other. The attractive forces that act on each object are always equal in size and act in opposite directions.

audible An audible sound is **a** one that can be heard by humans. It has a frequency in the range 20 Hz to 20 000 Hz; **b** one which is within the range of hearing of an organism.

auxin An auxin is a plant growth substance. Auxins function as plant hormones in that they are produced in one place and may have their effect distant from the source. They bring about growth by stimulating cell elongation and differentiation. Auxins are involved in tropisms – responses to external stimuli such as light, e.g. phototropism. They are also involved in leaf fall and fruit formation. Artificial, synthetic auxins are used in hormone rooting powders and can be used to produce seedless fruits.

background radiation Radioactivity is all around us. All living things and biomass are radioactive. Many rocks are also radioactive and the Earth is continually being bombarded by radiation from space. All these sources contribute to the background radiation, radioactivity that we are exposed to all the time.
Medical uses of radioactivity and radioactivity from nuclear power stations also contribute to the level of background radiation.

bacteria Bacteria are classified in the kingdom Prokaryotae. They are very small, lying within the range 10^{-7} m – 10^{-6} m. Bacteria show a variety of shapes including spherical (coccus), rod (bacillus), corkscrew (spirilla) and comma (vibrio). They reproduce asexually by binary fission. Pathogenic bacteria are responsible for many diseases but as a group they include many beneficial species, e.g. those responsible for the essential process of decomposition.

balanced diet A healthy balanced diet must include all the necessary daily food requirements, namely carbohydrates, fats proteins, vitamins, mineral salts, water and dietary fibre, in the correct proportions. It must take into account the age, occupation and lifestyle of the individual and will therefore vary from person to person.

barometer A barometer is a device that measures atmospheric pressure.

base A metal oxide which reacts with an acid to form a salt and water only. For example, copper(II) oxide reacts with sulphuric acid to produce copper(II) sulphate and water only.

battery A battery consists of a number of electrical cells. These cells are usually connected in series to give a higher voltage than that from a single cell.

battery farming The farming technique where animals are provided with an enclosed controlled environment, is known as battery farming. Most obvious examples of animals kept commercially in this way include hens and pigs.

bauxite The common ore of aluminium containing aluminium oxide with impurities such as iron(III) oxide. It is purified using sodium hydroxide solution to produce a white powder called alumina (aluminium oxide). It is then used in a smelter to produce aluminium.

beta A beta particle is a type of radioactive emission that consists of a high-energy electron. It is ejected from an unstable atomic nucleus when a neutron decays to a proton.

biceps The flexor muscle of the human arm that operates at the elbow joint is called the biceps. Contraction of the biceps flexes the arm.

big bang theory The theory that the whole universe started from an enormous explosion at a single point in space is known as the big bang theory.
Evidence to support this theory comes from the existence of microwave energy that permeates space and from the movement of the galaxies. When the paths of their movement are traced back, they all seem to have started from the same point in space.

bile Liver cells produce an alkaline secretion which is stored in the gall bladder. This solution is called bile. It contains pigments and sodium salts. It is released into the duodenum (first part of the small intestine) via the bile duct. Its function is to make the contents of the gut more alkaline and to emulsify the fats present in it. Both changes, brought about by the addition of bile, enhance the activity of enzymes that, having been made in the pancreas, are present in the duodenum. Firstly they have an optimum pH of 7–8 and the emulsification process dramatically increases the surface area of the fat which can then be more easily digested by the enzyme lipase.

binary fission Unicells reproduce asexually by mitosis. This type of asexual reproduction is called binary fission.

biodegradable Any substance that can be broken down by micro-organisms is described as being biodegradable.

biomass Biomass is the total dry mass of an organism.

biosphere The Earth's biosphere includes all those places, including the atmosphere, inhabited by organisms.

bitumen A thick black residue from fractional distillation of crude oil used for resurfacing roads.

blast furnace A furnace used for extracting metals such as iron. Blasts of hot air are blown through the furnace.

boiling point A liquid turns rapidly to its vapour at a fixed temperature called the boiling point, which varies with pressure. The lower the pressure the lower the boiling point.

bond breaking Breaking chemical bonds requires energy.

bonding The forces joining atoms together.

bond making Forming chemical bonds releases energy.

braking distance The braking distance of a vehicle is the distance it travels from when the brakes are applied to when the vehicle stops. The braking distance is proportional to the $(speed)^2$.

brine A solution of sodium chloride in water. It is produced when salt is extracted by solution mining.

Brownian motion When viewed under a microscope, smoke specks suspended in air are seen to move with a random jerky motion. This is known as Brownian motion after the biologist Robert Brown, who first observed it when looking at pollen grains in water.
The explanation of Brownian motion was proposed by Einstein: he argued that the particles of smoke or pollen are being bombarded by much smaller particles of air or water that must be moving at high speed in random directions.

bulimia Bulimia is an eating disorder where one of the symptoms is the intake of huge amounts of food followed by induced vomiting.

calcium carbonate A compound present in a wide range of rocks including chalk, limestone and marble. It is the remains of shells of animals.

calcium silicate This is the main chemical present in slag. It is produced in the blast furnace by the reaction of calcium oxide with the acidic oxide, silicon(IV) oxide.

$CaO + SiO_2 \rightarrow CaSiO_3$

It is used for resurfacing roads (road chippings) and as a phosphorus fertiliser.

camera A camera is an optical device that uses a convex lens to produce a real image on a film. The image produced is inverted and smaller than the original object.

capillary Capillaries are very small blood vessels with a wall which is only one cell thick. The arrangement of these cells creates gaps or 'windows' allowing exchange to take place between the blood and tissues. Diffusion of respiratory gases and food solutes is enhanced and phagocytes can escape and re-enter.

carbohydrates These are compounds of carbon, hydrogen and oxygen with the general formula $C_xH_yO_z$. Carbohydrates include simple sugars (monosaccharides), e.g. glucose, $C_6H_{12}O_6$; disaccharides, e.g. sucrose, $C_{12}H_{22}O_{11}$; and polymers, e.g. starch and cellulose.

carbon A non-metallic element. It can exist in different forms (called allotropes). Two of these are diamond and graphite. It is an unusual non-metal in that it can conduct electricity.

carbon cycle The carbon cycle describes the processes involved in the fixing and release of carbon.

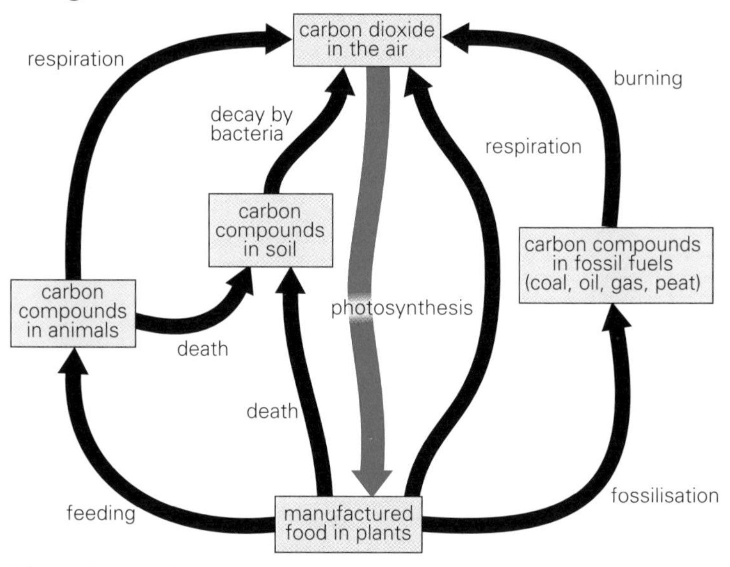

The carbon cycle

carbon dioxide Colourless gas produced when carbon or carbon compounds burn in a plentiful supply of oxygen. It is also formed when acid acts on a carbonate.

carbon monoxide Poisonous gas produced when carbon and carbon compounds burn in a limited supply of oxygen. Carbon monoxide is a good reducing agent.

carcinogen A carcinogen is something that causes cancer.

carnivore An animal which kills and feeds on another animal is called a carnivore. Examples include not only lions and tigers, but also spiders and frogs.

carrier This term is applied to any individual who is heterozygous for a genetic disease or disorder but appears to be normal (e.g. a person can carry the allele for cystic fibrosis and not know. If two such individuals have a child, there is a 1-in-4 probability of that child suffering from cystic fibrosis.)

cartilage Cartilage occurs between bones in synovial joints. It is flexible, hard wearing and serves to protect the bone tissue from damage. It also occurs in the nose, in the external ear, and between vertebrae. One group of fish is classified on the basis of having a cartilaginous skeleton.

casting Casting is one method of fossilisation where tissue is replaced by rock.

catalyst A substance which alters the rate of a reaction without being used up. Usually the reaction is speeded up. Catalysts are usually transition metals or transition metal compounds. An example of a catalyst is iron which catalyses the reaction of nitrogen and hydrogen to produce ammonia in the Haber process. Another example is vanadium(V) oxide, V_2O_5, which catalyses the reaction of sulphur dioxide and oxygen in the Contact process. A catalyst usually works either by providing a surface for the reaction to take place (iron) or by forming intermediate compounds (vanadium(V) oxide).

cathode A negatively charged electrode in electrolysis. The cathode has a surplus of electrons. At the cathode electrons are transferred from the cathode to the positively charged ion (cation) being discharged, e.g. $Cu^{2+} + 2e^- \rightarrow Cu$.

cell **a** in electricity, a cell consists of two electrodes in a liquid. A voltage exists between the electrodes that causes a current when they are connected by a conductor; **b** in biology, a cell is the basic unit of life. It is composed of some cytoplasm surrounded by a surface membrane. The cytoplasm contains a number of smaller structures that carry out particular functions, e.g. nucleus, ribosomes and mitochondria.

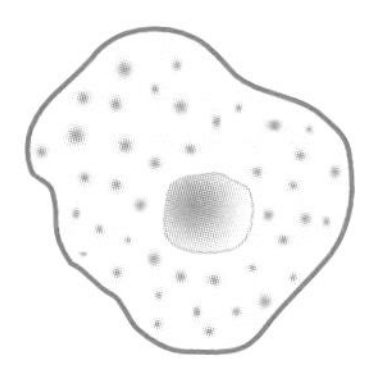

A typical animal cell

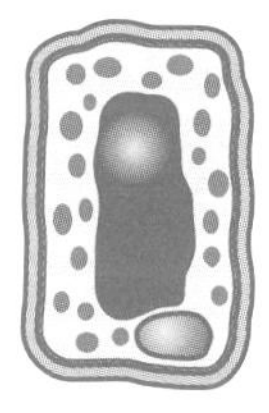

A typical plant cell

celsius The celsius temperature scale is based on the ice and steam points of water. The ice point is defined as 0 °C and the steam point as 100 °C. The interval between these points is divided into one hundred equal units on the measuring instrument, commonly a liquid-in-glass thermometer.

CFCs Chlorofluorocarbons are atmospheric pollutants. They are used in aerosols and refrigerators. They are involved in the destruction of the ozone layer and are partly responsible for increasing the rate of global warming.

charge Charge is a property of two of the particles that make up the atom. Electrons and protons have charge of opposite types. That on the electron is called negative and that on the proton is called positive.

chlorophyll Chlorophyll is a green pigment which is capable of absorbing light providing photosynthesis with a source of energy.

chloroplasts Chloroplasts are membrane-bound organelles found in the cytoplasm of plant cells. They are a characteristic feature of many plant cells, and are the site of photosynthesis.

cholesterol Cholesterol is a fat which, if not kept within set limits within the body, can cause circulatory problems. Some is needed by the body as it is a component of cell membranes.

chromatid (See **mitosis**.)

chromatography A way of separating mixtures, especially coloured substances, by letting them spread across a filter paper or through a powder. Each component in the mixture spreads at a different speed.

chromosome A chromosome is composed of DNA and a structural protein. Each chromosome consists of a series of genes.

chromosome number Each species of living thing has a characteristic number of chromosomes present in the nuclei of its body cells (e.g. 46 in human cells). In sex cells the chromosome number is halved (e.g. 23 in human eggs and sperm).
(See also **haploid** and **diploid**.)

cilia Cilia are microscopic hair-like structures associated with certain types of cells. If the ciliated cell is anchored, movement of the cilium causes the fluid around the cell to move, e.g. ciliated cells in the human respiratory tract. Movement of cilia on a free cell will pull or push the cell through the liquid it inhabits.

circuit A circuit is one or more conducting paths between the two electrodes of a cell or battery of cells.

circuit breaker A device used to cut off the voltage supply if a fault occurs in a circuit. One type is known as an RCCB, or residual current circuit breaker. This cuts off the voltage supply if a current passes to earth. Another type of circuit breaker acts like a fuse: it breaks the circuit if too large a current passes in the live wire.

classification Plants and animals can be placed in groups according to their characteristic features. Each classification group is called a taxon. There is a hierarchy of taxa. A kingdom is the largest taxon – a species is the smallest. Each division of a taxon produces smaller groups containing organisms that are more similar to each other.

clone When an organism reproduces asexually, the offspring have genes identical to those of their parent. A group of organisms with identical genes is called a clone. Cloning is used commercially to produce large numbers of 'products' with known, desirable characteristics.

coagulation Proteins consist of coiled chains. Heating, for example, can partially break up the protein irreversibly. This is called coagulation.

coil A coil is a metallic conductor with a number of loops.

coke An impure form of carbon made by heating coal out of contact with air.

combination The joining together (or combining) of atoms of different elements to form a compound. (See also **synthesis**.)

comet An object consisting mainly of frozen gases and dust that orbits the Sun. The orbit of a comet is highly elliptical and can be in any plane and either direction. Comets are visible as they pass close to the Sun. When visible, a comet consists of a head and a tail. The head is the solid matter and the tail is the matter that has been vaporized by energy absorbed from the Sun.

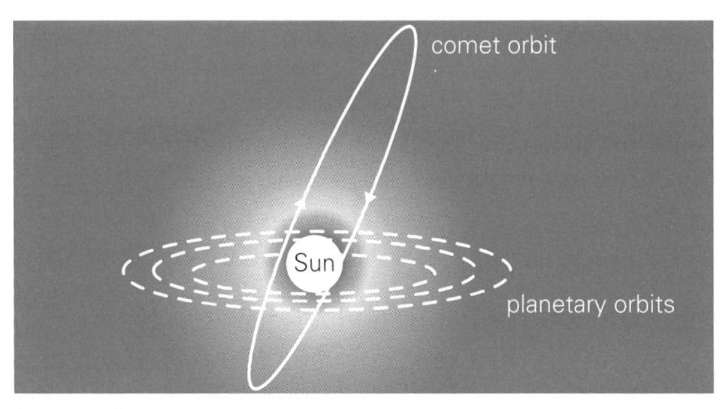

Orbits of the planets and a comet

community A community is a group of populations of plants, animals and microorganisms interacting within an habitat. One important interaction is based on feeding.

commutator A commutator is the part of an electric motor that passes the current from the carbon brushes to the coil. In a d.c. motor a split-ring commutator reverses the current in the coil once every half revolution to keep the coil turning in the same direction.

compensation point The outcome of photosynthesis reverses the outcome of aerobic respiration. The point where photosynthetic production of glucose exactly balances the glucose used by respiration is called the compensation point.

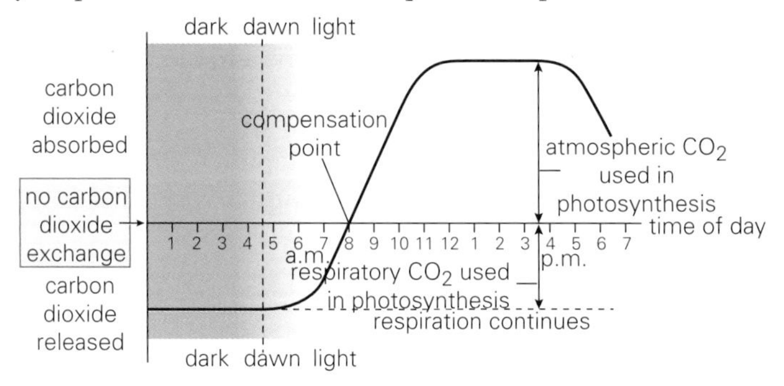

Carbon dioxide exchanged by a plant from midnight until 7 pm on a day in summer

competition Competition is the interaction between organisms for the resources found in the environment, e.g. plants compete for space, light, water and mineral nutrients.

complimentary base pair The organic bases found in a nucleic acid, e.g. DNA, always pair in a characteristic way, e.g. adenine and thymine. The pairing is compulsory. Each is known as a complementary pair.

component A component is a device in a circuit where energy is transferred from electricity into heat, light or movement.

compound A substance formed by joining atoms of different elements together.

compression A compression forms part of a longitudinal wave where the particles of material that transmit the wave are closer together than the equilibrium separation.

concave Concave describes the shape of a lens or other object where the centre is thinner than the outside.

concentration gradient A concentration gradient is a measure of the difference in concentration between two places with respect to the same substance.

condensation polymer A polymer produced by a series of condensation reactions. The monomer must contain two reactive groups. When each link is formed a small molecule is lost. Examples of condensation polymers are nylon and polyester.

condensation reaction A reaction between two smaller molecules to form a larger molecule, accompanied by the loss of a small molecule including water, e.g.

$$\text{acid} + \text{alcohol} \rightleftharpoons \text{ester} + \text{water}$$

condensing Changing a vapour (or gas) into a liquid. This change is accompanied by a giving out of energy.

conduction **a** in electricity, conduction occurs when charged particles move through a material. In a metal, conduction is due to the movement of free electrons. In an ionised gas or molten or dissolved electrolyte, conduction is due to both positively charged ions and negatively charged ions moving in opposite directions. **b** There are two mechanisms of thermal conduction. Energy is transferred from energetic particles to less energetic neighbouring particles through vibrations and collisions. In addition to this, free electrons transfer thermal energy in a metal by the process of diffusion. **c** in biology, water is transported in the xylem tissue of plants. This process is known as conduction.

conductor A material that allows charged particles to flow through it is an electrical conductor. A material that allows thermal energy to flow through it is a thermal conductor.

conglomerate A sedimentary rock consisting of pebbles cemented together by a matrix of fine material.

conservation Nature conservation is the maintenance of ecosystems, particularly those that may be under threat from Man's activities.

consolidation One of the stages in forming a sedimentary rock.

constant A constant has a fixed numerical value. An example is the product of volume and pressure for a fixed amount of gas whose temperature does not change.

constructive boundary When two plates are moving apart, hot molten rock comes to the surface and forms new igneous rocks. This occurs, for example, in the Atlantic Ocean, where American and African plates are moving apart.

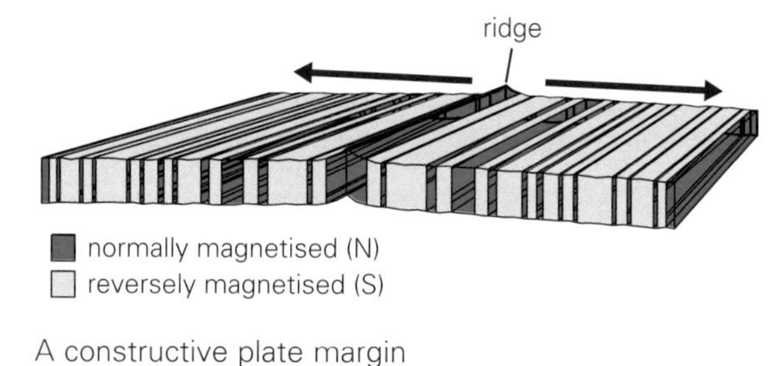

A constructive plate margin

consumer A consumer is an organism that feeds on ready-made food, i.e. other organisms. All non-photosynthetic organisms must be, by definition, consumers.

contraction The opposite of expansion, a contraction is a reduction in size often associated with a change in temperature. Most substances contract as the temperature is reduced. An exception to this is water: it expands as its temperature is reduced in the range 4.2 °C to 0 °C.

convection The movement of parts of a fluid (a liquid or a gas) due to changes in density is called a convection current. With the exception of water between the temperatures of 0 °C and 4.2 °C, heating a fluid causes an expansion and a decrease in density. This results in the less dense fluid rising above the surrounding, denser fluid. Cooling a fluid causes it to contract and become denser. The result of this is that it sinks through the surrounding, less dense, fluid.

convex Convex describes the shape of a lens or other object where the centre is thicker than the outside.

corrosion The wearing away of the surface of a metal by chemical reactions with oxygen and water. Rusting is an example of corrosion.

coulomb The unit of electrical charge is the coulomb (C). This is the quantity of charge that flows past a point when a current of 1 amp passes for 1 second. Charge and current are related by the equation: charge flow = current × time.

covalent A type of bonding involving the sharing of one or more pairs of electrons. The electrons are given by the atoms combining. The diagram shows covalent bonding in chlorine and oxygen molecules.

cracking The breaking down of long-chain hydrocarbon molecules with high temperatures and a catalyst to produce short molecules. These molecules are unsaturated and can be used to make polymers. (See also **saturated compound**.)

critical angle This applies when light meets a boundary between two materials and the speed of light in the material that it is travelling in is less than the speed of light in the material beyond the boundary. If the angle of incidence at the boundary is greater than the critical angle all the light is reflected. If the angle of incidence is less than the critical angle some light is reflected and some passes through.

crude oil (or petroleum) A complicated mixture of hydrocarbons produced by the action of high temperature and high pressure on the remains of sea creatures in the absence of air. It is trapped between impermeable rocks. The diagram shows how crude oil collects in the Earth with natural gas.

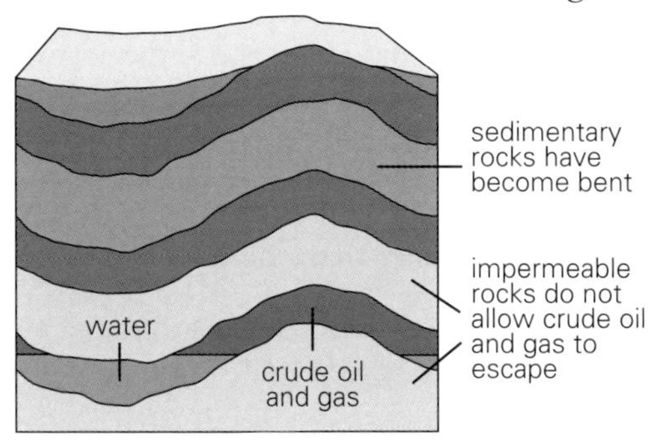

Processes which produce crude oil

crust The thin outer layer of the Earth.

cryolite A sodium aluminium fluoride used as a solvent for aluminium oxide in the extraction of aluminium. Cryolite used to be mined in Greenland. It is now made synthetically.

crystal A piece of solid substance that has a regular shape, flat sides, sharp edges and angles. The regular shape is caused by a regular arrangement of particles in the crystal.

crystallisation A process producing crystals. Crystals are formed when a molten substance is cooled or when a hot, saturated solution is cooled. Slow crystallisation produces large crystals and rapid crystallisation produces small crystals.

cubic A common shape for crystals, e.g. salt, sugar and magnesium oxide.

current A current is a flow of electric charge. The current in a metallic conductor is due to a flow of negatively charged electrons. That in a conducting gas or a molten or dissolved electrolyte is due to a flow of both positive and negative ions.

cycle In wave motion, one complete wave is called a cycle. In the case of a longitudinal wave, one cycle is a compression and a rarefaction. In a transverse wave, one cycle is a crest and a trough.

cytoplasm Cytoplasm is the term used to describe everything inside a cell except the nucleus.

decay Decay is another term for the process of decomposition brought about by microscopic organisms, e.g. bacteria and fungi.

decomposer A microscopic organism which reduces organic matter to inorganic matter is called a decomposer. Decomposers are active in the cycling of elements, e.g. carbon cycle and nitrogen cycle.

decomposition A chemical reaction that results in the breaking down of a substance into simpler substances. There are different types of decomposition – thermal decomposition (by heating), catalytic decomposition and electrolytic decomposition.

dehydration A reaction where water (or the elements of water – hydrogen and oxygen) is removed. For example, dehydration of sucrose, $C_{12}H_{22}O_{11}$ produces carbon.

denatured When enzymes are heated above about 40 °C the active sites are destroyed and the catalytic activity is destroyed.

dendrite A crystal skeleton formed when secondary growths form during crystallisation.

denitrifying bacteria Soil bacteria which break down nitrates in the soil releasing nitrogen gas into the atmosphere.

density The density of a material is the mass per unit volume. It is defined as *density* = *mass* ÷ *volume*, and measured in units of g/cm^3 or kg/m^3. When the density is high the particles are closely packed together.

deposition Formation of a deposit, i.e. a layer of precipitate.

destructive boundary A boundary where a denser oceanic plate moves under a continental crust plate. Rocks are returned to the magma for re-cycling.

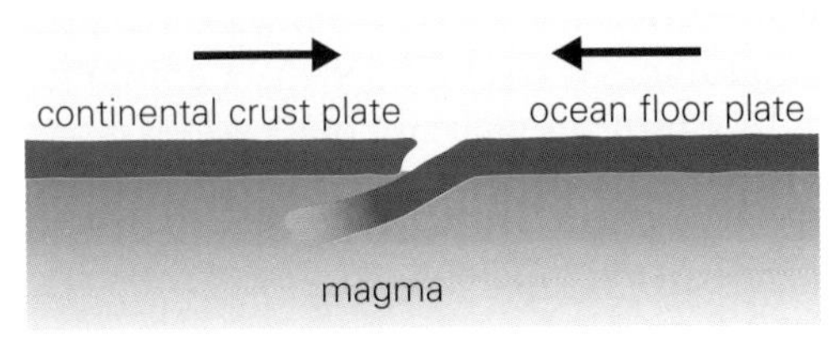

A destructive plate margin

detergent A detergent is a cleaning agent. There are two main types – soaps and soapless detergents.

diabetes There are two forms of diabetes. Insulin-dependent diabetes is caused by the self-destruction of insulin-producing beta cells in the pancreas. Non-insulin dependent diabetes is caused principally by obesity. In both cases the body's ability to control the concentration of blood-glucose is lost.

dialysis Dialysis is a physical process employed to remove solutes from the blood of patients with kidney failure. The patient's blood flows between selectively permeable membranes surrounded by a carefully controlled dialysis fluid containing useful substances at normal blood concentrations.

diaphragm The diaphragm forms a boundary between the thoracic and abdominal cavities of a mammal. It is composed of a sheet of fibrous tissues suspended from the body wall by muscle. It is active in the ventilation of the lungs.

1,2-dibromoethane The addition product formed when bromine reacts with ethene.

diesel One of the fractions produced on fractional distillation of crude oil.

diet (See **balanced diet**.)

diffraction Diffraction is the spreading out of a wave as it passes through a gap or past the edge of an obstacle. The amount of spreading depends on the size of the gap compared to the wavelength of the wave. For the maximum spreading, the gap size should be equal to the wavelength. Less spreading takes place when the gap size is greater than the wavelength.

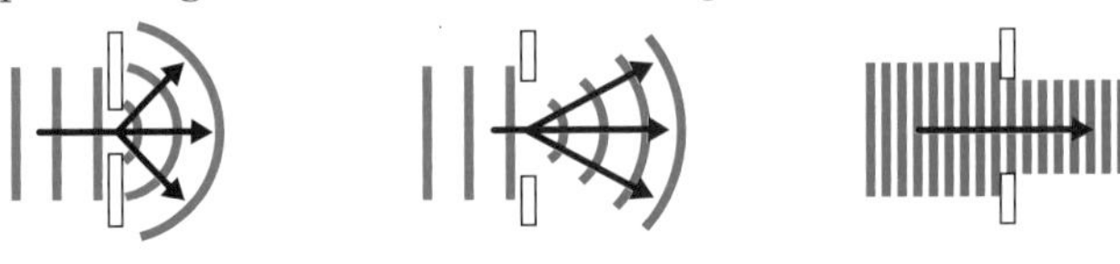

Diffraction of waves

diffusion The spreading out of a substance, due to the kinetic energy of its particles, to fill all the available space.

diffusion gradient A diffusion gradient is a measure of the rate at which particles will diffuse in a particular direction.

digestion Food material has to be broken down physically and chemically before it can be absorbed. Herbivores and carnivores chew food before swallowing it, breaking it up into smaller pieces. Enzymes present in the gut catalyse reactions during which large nutrient molecules are broken down into simpler, more soluble ones. In that state they can be absorbed through the lining of the gut. The reactions are hydrolyses, e.g.

starch $\xrightarrow{\text{amylase}}$ maltose + water

fat $\xrightarrow{\text{lipase}}$ fatty acids and glycerol + water

protein $\xrightarrow{\text{protease}}$ amino acids + water

diode A diode is a circuit component that only allows current to pass in one direction (the direction in which the diode allows current to pass is shown by an arrow on the circuit symbol). A light emitting diode (LED) is often used as an indicator to show when an appliance is switched on. Laser diodes are used to read compact discs (CDs).

The circuit symbol for a diode

diploid A diploid nucleus contains two of each kind of chromosome, 2n, e.g. 23 homologous pairs in humans.

direct current A direct current is a current that passes in one direction only. Cells and batteries are sources of direct current.

disaccharide A sugar formed by combining two monosaccharide molecules, with the elimination of a water molecule. The formula is $C_{12}H_{22}O_{11}$ and examples are sucrose and maltose.

discharging The conversion of an ion to a neutral atom at an electrode during electrolysis.

dislocation When a melt (molten substance) solidifies, crystals start to form at certain points in the melt. When these crystals meet, there is not a perfect fit. The imperfection where crystals meet is called a dislocation.

dispersion Dispersion is the separation of light into its constituent colours. It occurs when light passes through a prism or a diffraction grating. Dispersion also takes place when light passes through raindrops to produce a rainbow.

displacement The amount and direction of movement from the normal or rest position.

displacement reaction A reaction where one metal replaces another during a chemical reaction, e.g.

copper(II) sulphate + iron → copper + iron(II) sulphate

$$CuSO_4(aq) + Fe(s) \rightarrow Cu(s) + FeSO_4(aq)$$

The reaction occurs because iron is more reactive (higher in the reactivity series) than copper.

dissolving The process that occurs when a solute is added to a solvent and the solute disappears. The particles of the solute fit between the particles of the solvent. The solute can be recovered by evaporation.

distillation A process of purification involving boiling followed by condensation.

division of labour The work load needed to keep a cell or organism alive is shared out.

DNA Deoxyribonucleic acid (DNA), is found in chromosomes. The bases adenine, thymine, guanine and cytosine provide the genetic code which controls the chemistry of a cell and in so doing determines the features of the cell.

dominant A dominant allele always expresses itself (works) whether it is partnered with another like itself or with a recessive allele.

dormant A dormant organism is alive but shows suspended growth and has a reduced metabolism.

double circulation Blood passes through the heart twice on each complete circuit of the mammalian body. It passes through both the pulmonary circuit and the systemic circuit.

double helix The two nucleotide chains that make up the polymer of DNA are wound around each other to form a double helix.

ductile Metals are said to be ductile because they can be drawn into fine wires.

Earth The Earth is the planet that we inhabit. In electricity, the term refers to an electrical connection to the Earth.

echo A reflection of a wave is called an echo. The term is commonly used to refer to the reflection of a sound or ultrasound wave.

ecosystem The ecosystem is the sum total of all the living organisms and non-living factors in an environment and the way they interact.

effector An effector is a muscle or gland which brings about a change or response to a stimulus.

effervescence If a gas is produced during a chemical reaction, bubbles of gas can be seen to escape from the solution. This 'fizzing' is called effervescence. (The word is frequently confused with efflorescence, which is the loss of water of crystallisation from a hydrated compound.)

efficiency The efficiency of a device is a measure of the proportion or percentage of energy input that is transferred to a useful energy output. It is defined by the equation *efficiency = useful energy (or power) output ÷ total energy (or power) input*. A measurement of efficiency does not have a unit, it is just a ratio.

egg An egg is a female gamete or sex cell. It carries one complete set of single chromosomes – the maternal chromosomes.

elastic A material is described as being elastic if it returns to its original size and shape when a force that causes deformation is removed.

elastic limit The elastic limit of a sample of material is the maximum force that can be applied for the sample to keep its elastic property.

electrode The conducting rod or plate which carries electricity in and out of an electrolyte during electrolysis.

electrolysis The splitting up of an electrolyte, either molten or in aqueous solution, by electricity. For example, electrolysis of molten lead(II) bromide produces lead at the negative electrode and bromine at the positive electrode.

electrolyte A chemical compound which, in aqueous solution or when molten, conducts electricity and is split up by it. Acids, bases, alkalis and salts are electrolytes. Electrolytes contain free ions that are able to move through the electrolyte.

electromagnet An electromagnet is a coil of wire, normally wrapped on an iron core. It has a strong magnetic field when a current passes in the coil. Switching off the current causes the magnetic field to collapse.

electromagnetic induction A voltage is induced in a conductor when the magnetic field through it changes. This phenomenon is known as electromagnetic induction. The size of the induced voltage is proportional to the rate at which the magnetic field changes.

electromagnetic radiation Electromagnetic radiation travels as a transverse wave motion. The complete electromagnetic spectrum consists of gamma rays, X-rays, ultraviolet radiation, light, infra-red radiation, microwaves and radio waves. Gamma rays have the shortest wavelength and highest frequency. Radio waves have the longest wavelength and lowest frequency.

electron An electron is a fundamental particle. It carries a negative charge. Electrons are the outermost particles in atoms, they orbit the atomic nucleus.

electron micrograph An electron micrograph is a photograph of an image produced by an electron microscope.

electroplating Coating one metal with a thin layer of another by electrolysis. This is done to prevent corrosion or to make the metal more decorative.

electrostatic charge Charge that is not moving is called electrostatic. Electrostatic charge is created on insulators when they rub together. It is due to the transfer of electrons from one insulator to the other. Attractive and repulsive forces exist between two charged objects: objects with similar charges repel each other and those with opposite charges attract each other. A build-up of electrostatic charge on an object can create a high voltage that ionises the surrounding air and causes sparks; this is how lightning occurs.

element A pure substance made of one kind of atom. It cannot be split up into anything simpler without losing its characteristics. There are just over one hundred elements known.

embryo An embryo is the young developing plant or animal. It develops from a zygote. In mammals it attaches to the lining of the uterus, in birds it is contained by the egg shell and in plants it is found inside a seed.

emitter The term emitter is used in the contexts of nuclear radiation and infra-red radiation. A radioactive isotope can emit alpha, beta or gamma radiation or a combination of these. All objects emit infra-red radiation. Dark, dull surfaces are better emitters of infra-red radiation than light, shiny surfaces.

endoskeleton The term endoskeleton is applied when the skeletal framework underlies the muscles and other tissues. The skeleton is 'on the inside', e.g. mammalian skeleton.

endothermic reaction A reaction where energy is taken in from the surroundings. There are few common examples of endothermic reactions.

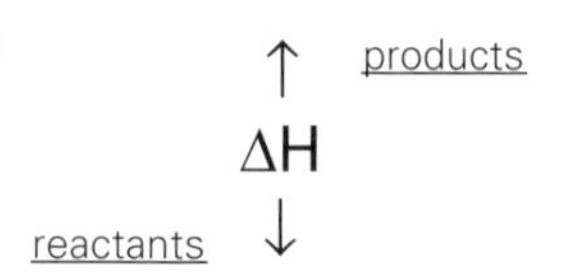

energy Any object that is capable of doing work is said to have energy.

energy change The difference between the energy in the products and the reactants.

energy level diagram A diagram showing the energy content at stages during a reaction.

environment The surroundings of a cell or organism provides their environment. A complex organism will have both an internal and an external environment.

enzymes Enzymes are proteins which act as biological catalysts.

equilibrium A reversible reaction is in equilibrium when the rate of the forward reaction equals the rate of the reverse reaction. If conditions change, the equilibrium may move to the right to produce more products or move to the left to produce more reactants.

erode Wear away.

erosion Process where rocks are worn away.

essential amino acids Those amino acids that a mammal cannot make and therefore must have as part of their diet are called essential amino acids.

ester An organic compound formed by the reaction of an acid and an alcohol.

acid + alcohol → ester + water

ethene The simplest alkene, with a formula C_2H_4.

eutrophication The result of the introduction of excessive amounts of nutrients, often nitrates and phosphates, into rivers or lakes. It results in over-production of plants, which die, and, as bacteria decay them, depletes oxygen.

evaporation The process by which a liquid changes to a vapour, due to particles leaving the surface of the liquid. This happens at temperatures below the boiling point but is fastest when the liquid is boiling.

evolution Evolution is one theory which offers an explanation for the way the different species of organisms present on Earth today came to be here.

excretion Metabolic reactions manufacture wastes that have to be got rid of. These wastes can be toxic if they build up and are called excretory products, e.g. urea and carbon dioxide, and are removed from the body by excretory organs. The whole process is called excretion.

exoskeleton Some invertebrates, e.g. crabs, beetles and snails, have a skeleton on the outside of their body. A hard, strong layer provides protection for the organism and a point to anchor muscles.

exothermic reaction A reaction where energy is lost to the surroundings. Examples include combustion reactions.

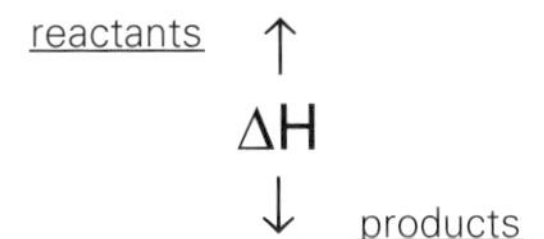

expansion An increase in the length or size of an object usually due to a change in temperature, though it can also be due to a reduction in temperature. Whilst most materials contract as the temperature is reduced, water expands when the temperature is reduced over the range 4.2 °C to 0 °C.

explosion A very rapid reaction accompanied by a large expansion in gases.

extinction Extinction is the condition which exists when all the members of a species have died and their genetic material has been lost.

extra-cellular The term extra-cellular means outside the cell, e.g. gut enzymes are extra-cellular.

extrusive Igneous rocks are formed when molten rock crystallises. Extrusive rocks are formed when this crystallisation occurs on the surface of the Earth. Basalt is an example of an extrusive igneous rock.

F_1 generation The F_1 is the first generation of offspring produced by two parents. The F_2 generation is the second generation of offspring.

faraday The faraday is a unit of electrical charge. One faraday (F) = 96 500 coulombs. For some purposes it is more convenient to use 1 F = 96 000 C as it simplifies arithmetic. A faraday can be defined as a mole of electrons. The quantity of electricity required to deposit 1 mole of sodium atoms from 1 mole of sodium ions, Na^+, is 1 F. The quantity of electricity required to deposit 1 mole of copper atoms from 1 mole of copper ions, Cu^{2+}, is 2 F.

fat Fats are natural esters formed from an organic acid and an alcohol called glycerol. Fats can be classified as saturated fats and unsaturated fats. Unsaturated fats contain carbon to carbon double bonds. Fats may be hardened by reaction with hydrogen using a nickel catalyst. This is used in the manufacture of margarine. Hydrolysis of a fat with alkali produces the sodium (or potassium) salt of the acid (sometimes called soap) and glycerol. This process is sometimes called saponification.

fault Break in rock caused by earth movement, e.g. the San Andreas Fault in California.

fermentation The process in which enzymes in yeast change glucose into ethanol and carbon dioxide, in the absence of oxygen.

fertilisation Fertilisation is the fusion of the haploid nuclei of two different gametes (sex cells), e.g. eggs and sperm.

fertiliser Composts and manures are natural fertilisers. Artificial fertilisers are produced by the chemical industry. Both are used to supplement the mineral nutrients present in a soil or replace those lost through crop removal.

fetus A fetus is a human embryo that has all the major structures of the adult present in rudimentary form.

field Any region where forces act on objects is called a field. Magnetic fields affect electric currents and magnetic objects, gravitational fields affect objects with mass and electric fields affect objects that are charged.

filtering (or **filtration**) A method of separating a solid from a liquid.

flexor muscle A flexor muscle bends a limb at a joint. (See **biceps**.)

food chain A food chain represents a sequence of organisms in a feeding relationship, e.g.
plankton → water flea → stickleback → heron

food web A food web arises when one producer or consumer can be eaten by more than one consumer. It represents a pattern of interconnected food chains.

force A force is a push or a pull. Forces are caused by objects and act on other objects. If object **A** exerts a force on object **B**, then **B** exerts an equal-size force on **A** in the opposite direction.

formula mass Mass in grams of quantity of material represented by a formula, e.g. formula mass of carbon dioxide, CO_2, is 44 g ($C = 12$, $O = 16$, therefore $CO_2 = 12 + 32 = 44$).

fossil The remains of plant and animal bodies which have not decayed and disappeared but have been preserved. Fossils may be found in sedimentary and metamorphic but not igneous rocks.

fossil fuel Fuels such as coal, oil and natural gas produced in the Earth from organic matter trapped in sediments over long periods of time.

fovea (See **retina**.)

fractional distillation A method of separating liquids with different boiling points.

free electron In a metal, some of the outermost electrons from each atom are able to move about within the body of the metal. They are called free electrons and they are responsible for the conduction of electricity and thermal energy.

freezing When a liquid changes to a solid at the freezing point.

frequency The number of cycles of a wave that pass any point in one second is called the frequency of the wave motion. Frequency is measured in hertz (Hz).

friction Friction is the name of the force that opposes two surfaces from slipping and sliding over each other.

fruit A fruit is formed by the modification of the wall of the ovary of a flower after fertilisation has taken place. It contains the seed(s).

fuel A substance which burns to produce energy.

fuse In electricity, a fuse is a length of thin wire placed in series with the live or positive conductor. If the current becomes dangerously high, the fuse melts, breaking the circuit. It is designed to protect against fire hazard in the connecting wires. Together with the earth wire, it also protects users of mains appliances from electrocution.

fusion When two atomic nuclei approach each other at high speed, they may fuse together. This is known as a fusion reaction. It results in the release of energy when less massive nuclei fuse, but it requires energy to make more massive nuclei fuse. Fusion of less massive nuclei is the reaction that takes place in stars.

galaxy A galaxy is a collection of stars, held together by the gravitational forces between them, e.g. the Milky Way.

galvanising The protection of iron or steel by coating with zinc. Even if the surface is scratched no rusting of steel takes place because zinc is more reactive than iron, so corrodes at the expense of the steel. Galvanising is used for fences, vulnerable steel plates in a car, etc. It is not used for food cans because zinc compounds are poisonous.

gamete A gamete is a sex cell, e.g. a sperm, egg, or particular nuclei found inside pollen grains or ovules.

gamma ray A high-energy, short wavelength form of electromagnetic radiation emitted when an unstable nucleus changes to a more stable form. It may be accompanied by the emission of other types of nuclear radiation.

gas A state of matter where the particles have a lot of kinetic energy and are widely spaced.

gaseous exchange This process involves the exchange of carbon dioxide and oxygen gases, needed for biological processes such as respiration and photosynthesis. In mammals, it takes place at the inner surface of the lungs. In land plants, it takes place through the damp surfaces of the cells inside leaves.

Geiger-Müller tube A detector of nuclear radiation.

gene A gene is a section of the nucleic acid DNA of a chromosome which on its own, or with associated genes, determines a particular characteristic. It consists of genetic coding that directs the production of enzymes that control the chemistry responsible for that characteristic.

generator A generator is a device that generates electricity. A power station generator consists of an electromagnet that rotates inside sets of copper conductors. The movement of the magnetic field causes a voltage to be induced in the copper conductors.

genetic engineering This is the technology which allows a gene (DNA) from one organism to be introduced into another organism.

genotype The genetic make-up of an organism. Symbols are used to represent the alleles present for a particular gene.

geostationary A satellite that has an orbit time around the Earth of 24 hours is geostationary. It remains above the same point on the Earth's surface. Geostationary satellites are used in telecommunications.

geothermal Energy extracted from hot underground rocks is called geothermal energy.

geotropism Geotropism is a plant growth response to gravity. Roots are positively geotropic and shoots are negatively geotropic.

germination Germination involves the initial growth and development going on inside a seed or spore. During this period the growing organism uses up stored food reserves. Germination is considered to be over once the organism has become established and either manufactures its own food by photosynthesis, or absorbs food from its environment.

giant structure This is a crystal structure in which all of the particles are linked together in a network of bonds extending throughout the crystal, e.g. diamond. A substance with a giant structure will have a high melting and boiling point as large amounts of energy are required to break down giant structures. Giant structures can be composed of ions (e.g. sodium chloride) or atoms (e.g. diamond).

glucose (See **carbohydrates**.)

gravitational force There is an attractive force between any two objects called a gravitational force. The size of the force increases with increasing mass and decreases with increasing separation.

gravitational potential energy Gravitational potential energy is the energy an object has due to its position. Close to the Earth's surface, a change in position results in a change of gravitational potential energy equal to *weight* × *change in height*.

greenhouse effect This is caused by atmospheric carbon dioxide and other 'greenhouse gases' reducing heat loss from the atmosphere into space. An increase in these gases will result in global warming.

group A vertical column in the Periodic Table (see p. 76).

guard cells (See **stomata**.)

habitat The habitat of an organism is the place where it lives. Its habitat will provide a particular environment that includes a combination of factors, biotic and abiotic, that enable the organism to live successfully.

haematite One of the common iron ores containing iron(III) oxide.

haemoglobin Haemoglobin is an iron-containing blood pigment that combines reversibly with oxygen. It is found in red blood cells.

$$\text{oxygen} + \text{haemoglobin} \underset{\text{low oxygen availability, e.g. near to actively respiring tissue}}{\overset{\text{high oxygen availability, e.g. near to lung air spaces}}{\rightleftharpoons}} \text{oxyhaemoglobin}$$

half-life The half-life of a radioactive isotope is the average time it takes for the number of undecayed nuclei in a sample to halve.

halogen An element in group 7 of the Periodic Table (see p. 76). The word halogen means salt-producer. Common halogens are fluorine, chlorine, bromine and iodine. The reactivity of halogens decreases down the group. Each halogen atom has seven electrons in the outer energy level (shell).

haploid A haploid nucleus contains only one of each kind of chromosome, n, e.g. 23 singles in humans.

hard water Water which does not lather well with soap but forms scum. Hard water is caused by dissolved calcium and magnesium compounds. These compounds get into the water as it trickles through rocks in the ground. Hard water can be divided into temporary hardness and permanent hardness.

helium A noble gas (group 0 in the Periodic Table (see p. 76)) which is used for balloons because it has a low density.

herbivore An animal which feeds exclusively on plant material is called a herbivore. Mammalian herbivores have a set of teeth that is adapted to grind plant tissue to a pulp.

hertz Frequency, the number of events per second, is measured in hertz (Hz).

heterozygous This is the condition where an organism has two different alleles for a particular gene.

hibernate The body chemistry of an hibernating organism slows down, enabling the organism to survive periods of low temperature. Shrews, hedgehogs and hamsters are examples of animals that hibernate.

homeostasis This is the ability which complex organisms have to maintain a stable internal environment for their cells and tissues.

homeothermy Homeothermic organisms maintain a constant body temperature, e.g. human body temperature, 37 °C.

homozygous This is the condition where an organism has two of the same alleles for a particular gene.

hormone Hormones are chemical compounds secreted directly into the blood system by ductless glands. They function as 'chemical messengers' which affect target organs elsewhere in the body, e.g. adrenaline, produced in the adrenal glands, affects the heart, rate and depth of breathing, and the state of blood vessels.

host (See **parasite**.)

hydrated A hydrated substance contains water.

hydraulic In hydraulics a liquid is used to transmit pressure. Liquids used in hydraulic machinery can be made to exert very large forces by applying the pressure over a large area.

hydrocarbon A hydrocarbon is a compound of only two elements – carbon and hydrogen.

hydroelectric In a hydroelectric power station, electricity is generated from moving water. The energy of the moving water can be produced from the natural flow of a river or it can be produced from releasing water stored in a reservoir and allowing it to fall down pipes.

hydrogen The gas with the lowest density. It burns with a squeaky pop when a lighted splint is put into it. It used to be used for airships but is no longer used as it is highly flammable. It is still used for weather balloons.

hydrogen chloride Hydrogen chloride is a colourless gas which dissolves in water to form hydrochloric acid. It is formed when concentrated sulphuric acid is added to salt. It is sometimes called 'salt-gas'.

hydrogenation The reaction of a natural fat or oil with hydrogen, in the presence of a nickel catalyst, to form margarine.

hydrolysis A reaction in which a large molecule is split into two smaller molecules by reaction with a water molecule.

hydrolytic (See **hydrolysis**.)

igneous Rocks that have cooled and solidified as crystals from molten rock, e.g. granite.

immiscible Two liquids which do not completely mix, e.g. oil and water.

immunisation Immunisation or vaccination is achieved by injecting a vaccine into a healthy individual. The antigens in the vaccine trigger the immune response offering the individual some protection at a later date because of the memory cells produced.

impermeable rocks Rocks which do not allow water or gas to pass through them.

in vitro fertilisation (IVF) IVF involves eggs taken from a female being fertilised outside the body before being returned to a receptive uterus.

indicator A chemical that can show if a substance is acidic or alkaline by changing colour. For example, litmus turns red in acids and blue in alkali.

infra-red Infra-red radiation is the part of the electromagnetic spectrum with a wavelength longer than that of light and shorter than that of microwaves. It causes heating when it is absorbed and is also used for remote switching of domestic appliances such as televisions.

inner core The centre of the Earth is composed of an inner core and an outer core.

insulation In electricity, insulation is a very high-resistance material such as pvc that is used around conductors to prevent short-circuits. Thermal insulation is any material used to reduce the flow of thermal energy from a hot object or to a cold object.

insulin Insulin is a hormone secreted by cells in the pancreas. It causes liver cells to remove soluble glucose from the blood and convert it to insoluble glycogen.

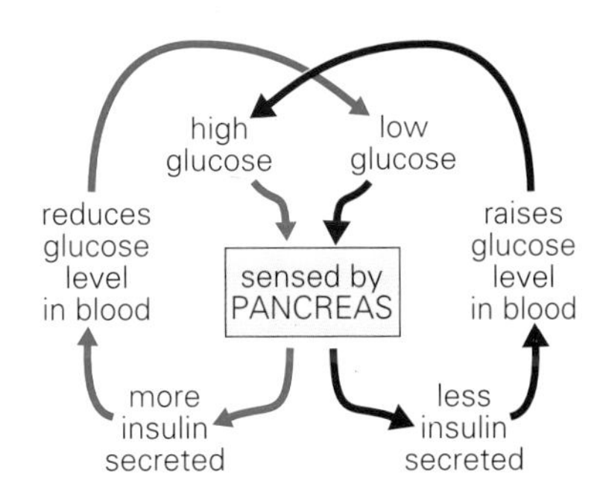

How feedback controls blood glucose level

intrusion A body of molten rock which forces its way between layers of rock.

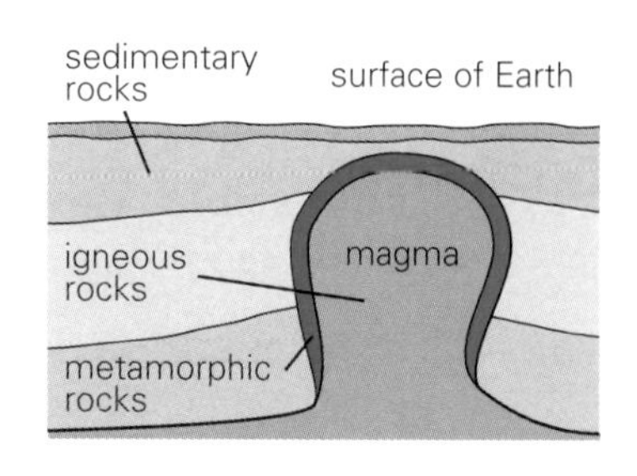

An intrusion

intrusive Igneous rocks which crystallise inside the Earth, e.g. granite. They reach the surface only when rocks above them are eroded.

invertebrate Animals without a backbone are called invertebrates. Examples make up 95% of animal species.

ion A positively or negatively charged particle formed when an atom or group of atoms loses or gains electrons, e.g. chloride Cl^-, aluminium Al^{3+} and sulphate SO_4^{2-}.

ionic The type of bonding involving complete transfer of one or more electrons from a metal atom to a non-metal atom. Doing this forms ions. The ions are held together in a giant structure or lattice by strong electrostatic forces.

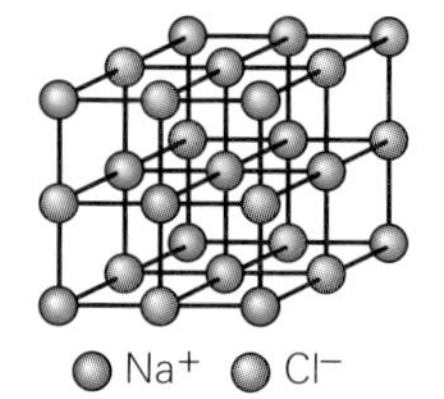

Sodium chloride lattice (not to scale)

ionosphere The ionosphere is an ionised layer in the atmosphere that reflects low frequency radio waves.

isotope These are atoms with the same atomic number, but different mass numbers. For example, two isotopes of chlorine are chlorine-35 and chlorine-37. Both contain 17 protons and 17 electrons. Chlorine-35 contains 18 neutrons and chlorine-37 contains 20 neutrons.

joule The joule is the unit of work and energy. One joule is the work done (and energy transfer) when a force of one newton moves a distance of one metre in its own direction.

kelvin The unit of absolute temperature. On the kelvin scale the freezing point of water (0 °C) is 273 K and the boiling point of water (100 °C) is 373 K.

kidney The human kidney is an organ which removes urea and other excretory materials, and some water, from the blood that flows through it to make urine. Tubules in the kidney, selectively reabsorb glucose and the correct amount of water and salt for the body to function properly.

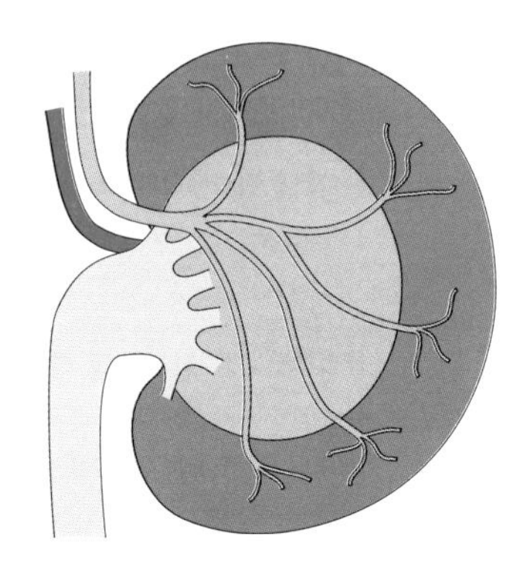

Section through a kidney

kilogramme The kilogramme (kg) is the SI unit of mass.

kilowatt A power of one thousand watts is equal to one kilowatt (kW).

kilowatt-hour The amount of energy supplied through the electricity and gas mains to homes and workplaces is measured in kilowatt-hours. One kilowatt-hour is the energy transfer by a one kilowatt appliance in one hour.

kinetic energy Kinetic energy is the energy that an object has due to its movement. It is calculated from the formula $kinetic\ energy = \frac{1}{2} \times mass \times (speed)^2$.

kingdom (See **classification**.)

lamp A device that is designed to transfer energy from electricity into light.

lattice Ionic bonding leads to a crystalline structure called a lattice. A lattice is a giant structure of ions. Sodium chloride and magnesium oxide have the same lattice structure.

leaching Leaching is the removal of soluble material by a solvent, e.g. the removal of nutrients from soils by rainwater.

ligament Bones are attached to other bones in a skeleton by ligaments. A ligament is formed from tissues that secrete protein. Ligaments can resist stretching but do show some elasticity.

light The part of the electromagnetic spectrum that is detected by the human eye. It lies between ultraviolet and infra-red radiation.

light dependent resistor The resistance of a light dependent resistor (LDR) depends on its illumination. As the light level increases, its resistance falls.

light emitting diode A light emitting diode (LED) gives out light when it is conducting. Like other diodes, it only allows current to pass in one direction, shown by the arrow on the symbol.

limewater A saturated solution of calcium hydroxide. It turns milky when carbon dioxide passes through it. The precipitate formed is calcium carbonate.

$$Ca(OH)_2(aq) + CO_2(g) \rightarrow CaCO_3(s) + H_2O(l)$$

limit of proportionality On a graph showing the relationship between the extension of a material and the applied force, the limit of proportionality is the point at the end of the straight line region. Beyond this point the extension is no longer proportional to the force.

limiting factor A limiting factor is something which holds back a process, e.g. low light intensity can limit the rate of photosynthesis shown by a plant. In phase I of the following graph, increasing the light intensity increases the rate of photosynthesis. In this phase, light is limiting. In phase II, light is less limiting, and in phase III, light is not limiting – increasing the light intensity does not change the rate of photosynthesis.

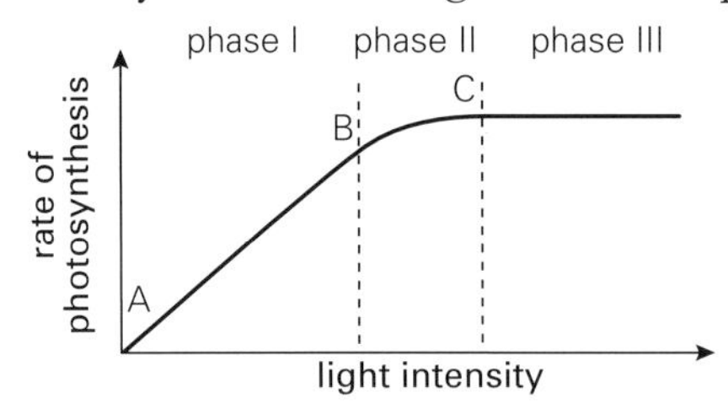

Relationship between the rate of photosynthesis and light intensity

liquid A state of matter. The particles are close together, irregularly arranged and moving over each other.

live Energy flows along the live conductor from the mains supply to an appliance. The potential difference between the live conductor and earth varies between +240 V and −240 V.

lock and key model The 'lock and key' model is one way used to explain enzyme action. The protein of the enzyme acts as the 'lock' and the substrate is the 'key'. For the interaction to be successful the 'key' must fit the 'lock' perfectly.

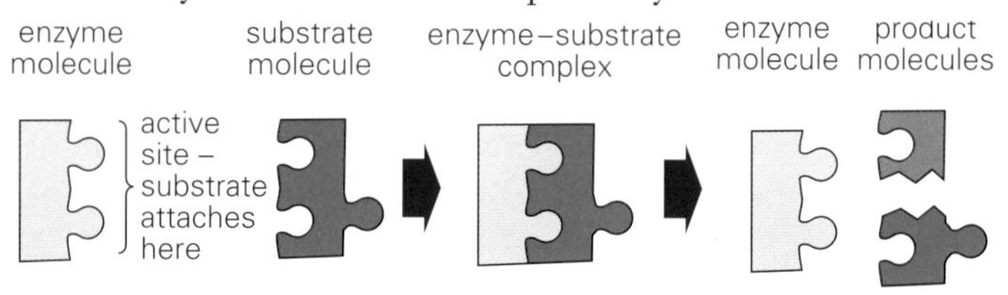

How an enzyme works

locus The specific position on a chromosome occupied by a gene is its locus.

longitudinal A wave motion where the oscillation is parallel to the direction of wave travel, for example a sound wave.

luminous An object that emits light is luminous.

lung A mammal has a pair of lungs located in the thorax. The internal surface of a lung is extremely large, thin and moist with a rich blood supply. This is the gaseous exchange surface for the animal connected to the atmosphere by means of tubes.

Atmosphere→trachea→bronchus→bronchioles→alveolar surface

lymph Lymph is a colourless liquid which is found in the lymphatic system of a vertebrate. It is formed from the fluid that escapes from capillaries.
The lymphatic system composed of ducts and lymph nodes, returns fluid and proteins to the blood.

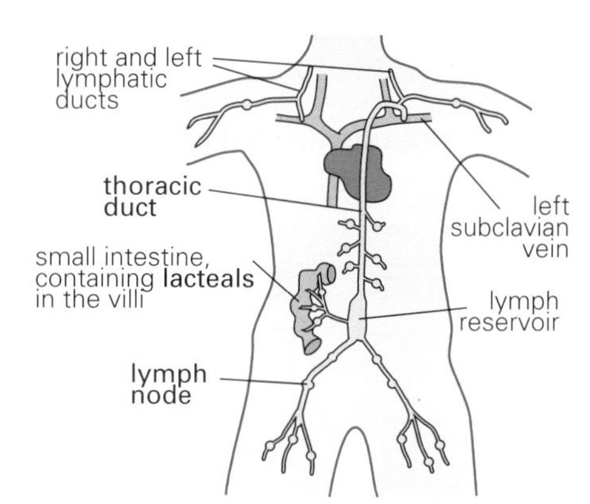

The lymphatic system in Man

lymphocyte (See **antibodies**.)

magma Semi-molten rock under the solid crust of the Earth.

magnetic This applies to any object or material that is attracted or repelled by a magnet. Common magnetic materials include iron, steel, cobalt and nickel.

magnetic field A magnetic field is an area where a magnetic material experiences a force. Magnetic fields exist around permanent magnets, electromagnets and electric currents.

main sequence A phase in the life cycle of a star. In its main sequence, a star generates energy by the fusion of hydrogen nuclei into helium nuclei. Our Sun is currently in its main sequence.

malleable Metals are malleable because they can be beaten into thin sheets.

malnutrition Malnutrition is a condition caused by an inappropriate diet. It is possible to eat too little or too much of particular parts of the diet. The two extremes are starvation and obesity.

mantle The part of the Earth between the crust and the core.

marble A metamorphic rock produced by the action of high temperatures and high pressures on limestone.

mass The term mass refers to an object. It is a measure of the amount of material that makes up the object. The unit of mass is the kilogramme.

mass number Mass number is the total number of nucleons (protons and neutrons) in an atomic nucleus.

measurement The value of any quantity that has been measured.

meiosis (reduction division) Meiosis is the type of cell division that produces cells that have half the number of chromosomes of their parent cell. It is achieved by the separation of the member chromosomes of each of the homologous pairs present in a nucleus. It is important in the formation of gametes (sex cells). This avoids constant doubling-up of chromosome number each generation. Meiosis is also an important way in which variation can arise. This is achieved in two ways. Firstly, an exchange of pieces of chromosomes can occur between paternal and maternal members of the same pair of chromosomes. Secondly, the paternal and maternal chromosomes of each pair are separated randomly.

melting A solid changes to a liquid at the melting point.

membrane A cell membrane is a thin sheet-like structure formed from fat and protein molecules. Membranes can change their shape, break down and be reformed. They are selectively permeable.

menstruation Menstruation occurs when the blood progesterone level drops causing the lining of the uterus to break down. The tissues are lost, through the vagina, with a considerable amount of blood.

meristem A meristem is a region of plant tissue that continues to show cell division and subsequent growth, for the lifetime of the plant. Examples are found at the tips of roots and shoots.

metabolism All the chemical reactions that go on in a living organism add up to its metabolism. Metabolism includes synthetic and breakdown processes.

Metabolism = Anabolism + Catabolism
'synthetic' 'breakdown'

metalloid Elements with properties between those of metals and non-metals. Germanium is a metalloid.

metamorphic Rocks that were originally either igneous or sedimentary and which have been altered by the effects of high temperatures and high pressures, e.g. marble. The process producing metamorphic rocks is called metamorphosis.

meter An instrument used for measuring a physical quantity. For example, a forcemeter measures force and an ammeter measures current.

methane The simplest member of the alkane family with a formula CH_4. It is the major component of natural gas.

metre The SI unit of length.

microbe This is a general term used to describe microscopic organisms including algae, bacteria, fungi, protozoa and viruses.

micropropagation This is a technique that can be used to produce a large clone from a small piece of parent tissue.

microwave Microwaves are short wavelength radio waves. In the electromagnetic spectrum, they occur between infra-red and radio waves.

mineral A naturally occurring substance of which rocks are made.

mitochondrion A mitochondrion is a cell organelle that contains the enzymes needed for aerobic respiration. Mitochondria are most numerous in those cells that have a high energy requirement, e.g. nerve cells.

mitosis When a cell divides by mitosis it produces two identical copies of itself. Mitosis follows four stages. These are:

- replication – the DNA of each chromosome is copied to form two chromatids;
- spindle formation – fibres of protein are arranged to enable separation of chromatid pairs;
- contraction of spindle fibres – separates the members of each chromatid pair;
- division of the cytoplasm.

Mohs scale A scale of hardness of materials. Diamond, with a value of 10, is the hardest natural substance.

molar volume One mole (6×10^{23} particles) of any gas occupies 24 dm^3 at room temperature and atmospheric pressure.

mole The amount of substance containing 6×10^{23} particles.

molecular A type of structure that is made up of molecules. In a sample of oxygen gas, there are strong forces between the oxygen atoms within each molecule. There are weak forces between the molecules. A substance with a molecular structure has low melting and boiling points.

molecule The smallest part of an element or compound which can exist on its own.

moment The moment of a force is the effect it has in turning an object around a pivot. The size of the moment is calculated using *moment = size of force × perpendicular distance from the line of action of the force to the pivot* and is measured in Nm.

monoculture This is the name given to the farming practice where large areas of land are given over to one type of crop, often in successive years, e.g. large areas of cereal.

monohybrid inheritance Monohybrid inheritance is the inheritance of a single pair of alleles. A monohybrid cross would involve parental varieties differing in a single character.

monomer A small molecule which joins together with other molecules to produce a polymer. Ethene is the monomer used to manufacture poly(ethene).

monosaccharide A simple sugar with a formula $C_6H_{12}O_6$. Glucose and fructose are two examples.

Moon The Moon is the Earth's natural satellite. Its origin is not known, but dating of Moon rock indicates that it is younger than the Earth.

motor A motor consists of a coil of wire placed within a magnetic field. The coil rotates when a current passes in it.

mucus A fluid secreted by cells in mucous membranes to lubricate the digestive tract and air tubes.

multicellular A multicellular organism is composed of many cells.

mutagen (See **mutation**.)

mutation Mutation is usually a random process of genetic change but sometimes it is caused by a factor known as a mutagen. The cell or organism produced by mutation is known as a mutant.

natural frequency The natural frequency of vibration of an object is the frequency it vibrates at when it is displaced from its normal position and then released. The larger and more massive the object, the lower the natural frequency of vibration.

natural polymer A polymer which occurs in nature, e.g. starch, cellulose.

natural selection Natural selection is a hypothesis that Darwin used to explain evolution. There are five major points in the theory:

i variation exists in the offspring of a sexually reproducing organism;
ii competition occurs for the resources in the environment of an organism;
iii some variants are at an advantage and compete successfully for the resources;
iv those that succeed survive and reproduce passing on the advantageous characteristics;
v over several generations the proportion of organisms with the advantageous characteristics will increase at the expense of those without. Some genotypes will be 'naturally selected', leading to their survival, others to extinction.

negative The pole of a cell or battery that repels negative charges and attracts positive charges.

negative feedback This is one of the important mechanisms in homeostasis. By producing more of something, the source eventually causes its own shutdown. The fluctuations are kept within narrow limits.

neurone A neurone is a nerve cell. There are several different types of neurone in the human body. The sensory neurone carries impulses from a sense organ to the central nervous system. A motor neurone carries impulses from the central nervous system to an effector such as a muscle or gland. A relay neurone passes impulses between neurones.

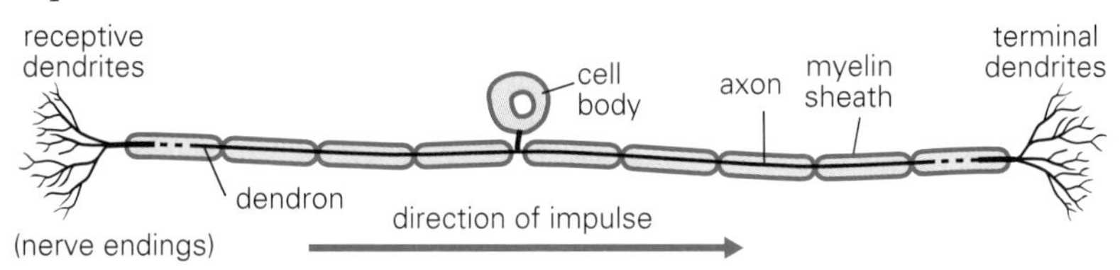

A sensory neurone

neutral a in mains electricity, the neutral connection is the conductor that completes the circuit from the live, through the appliance back to the mains supply; **b** in electrostatics, an object is neutral if its positive charge is balanced by its negative charge. **c** in chemistry, a neutral substance has a pH value of 7.

neutralisation A reaction in which an acid reacts with a base or alkali.

neutron An atomic particle found in the nucleus. It is similar in mass to a proton but has no charge.

newton The newton is the unit of force. One newton (1 N) is the force required to accelerate a mass of 1 kg at 1 m/s^2.

nitrate Nitrates are formed in reactions with nitric acid. Plants absorb nitrates in solution through the roots to provide the nitrogen essential for plant growth.

nitrifying bacteria A group of soil bacteria which convert ammonia into nitrates.

nitrogen cycle The processes involved in the fixing and release of nitrogen, the commonest gas in the atmosphere.

nitrogen-fixing bacteria A group of bacteria which fix gaseous nitrogen into nitrogen-containing substances, making nitrogen available to plants.

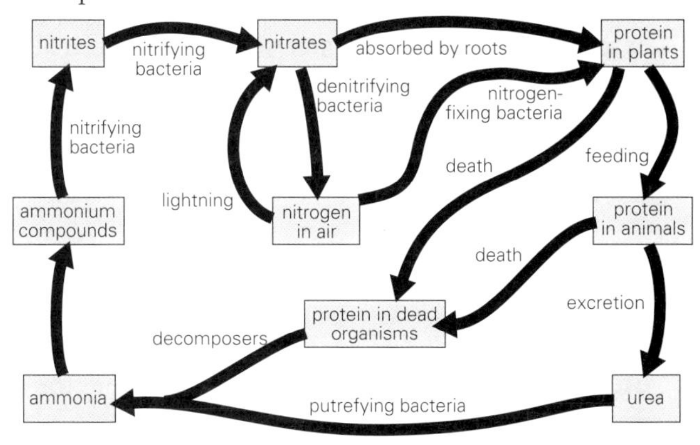

The nitrogen cycle

noble gas An element in group 0 of the Periodic Table (see p. 76).

non-metal Most of the elements are metals with characteristic properties, e.g. shiny, high density, good conductors of heat and electricity. Non-metals, e.g. carbon and sulphur, form acidic oxides, whilst metals form alkaline or neutral oxides.

nucleon A nuclear particle that is either a proton or a neutron.

nucleotide A nucleotide is a large molecule formed from three smaller molecules namely, a base containing nitrogen, a 5-carbon sugar and a phosphate group. Nucleotides can link together to form a chain that is sometimes called a strand. DNA contains two such strands.

nucleus **a** in physics, in an atom, the nucleus is the central part of the atom consisting of neutrons and protons; **b** in biology, the nucleus is sometimes described as the control centre of the cell. A membrane separates it from the cytoplasm of the cell. Chromosomes carrying the genetic code for the cell are contained within the membrane.

nutrient Nutrients are the inorganic molecules and ions that photosynthetic organisms need to manufacture organic molecules. Non-photosynthetic organisms consume those organic molecules as food chemicals. Both types of organism use the organic molecules as sources of energy or as building blocks to form more protoplasm.

nutrition Nutrition is the way in which organisms obtain their food. Green plants manufacture theirs from inorganic compounds by photosynthesis. Non-green plants and animals have to have ready-made food in the form of plant and animal tissue.

nylon A number of condensation polymers formed by reaction of molecules containing $-NH_2$ and $-COCl$ groups.

obesity Obesity is an eating disorder where the individual becomes extremely overweight.

oesophagus The oesophagus is part of the alimentary canal. It is a muscular tube that conducts food from the mouth to the stomach. Food passes along it as a result of pulses of muscular contraction known as peristalsis.

ohm The ohm (Ω) is the unit of resistance. One ohm is the resistance of a conductor that carries a current of 1 A when the potential difference across it is 1 V.

omnivore An omnivore is an animal that eats a diet containing both plant and animal material. Humans are omnivores although some choose to be vegetarian.

open cast Mining minerals by removing soil and surface rocks and digging out with an excavator. The soil and surface rocks can be replaced and the landscape restored. Open cast mining is possible when the rocks required are close to the surface.

orbit The path of any object that moves around another object, for example an electron around a nucleus or a planet around the Sun.

organ An organ is a group of tissues that collectively perform a specific function, e.g. lung, heart, leaf.

organ system An organ system is a group of organs that collectively perform a specific function, e.g. alimentary canal system, cardiovascular system, flower.

organelle A cell organelle is a very small structure that has a specific function. Many cell organelles are not visible with the light microscope. Examples of organelles include the nucleus, ribosomes, mitochondria and chloroplasts.

organic compounds Compounds of carbon, with other elements such as hydrogen, oxygen, nitrogen etc, present in living matter.

organism An organism is a collection of organ systems, which functions as a single individual.

oscillation A repetitive to-and-fro motion about a fixed point.

osmoreceptor Sensory structures that are sensitive to changing proportions of water and dissolved solutes are called osmoreceptors. There are cells present in the human brain that monitor how much water there is in the blood plasma. They assist in the homeostatic control of body water.

osmosis When a region of higher water concentration (A) is separated from one with a lower water concentration (B), by a selectively permeable membrane, the net movement of water is from A to B. It is a special kind of diffusion.

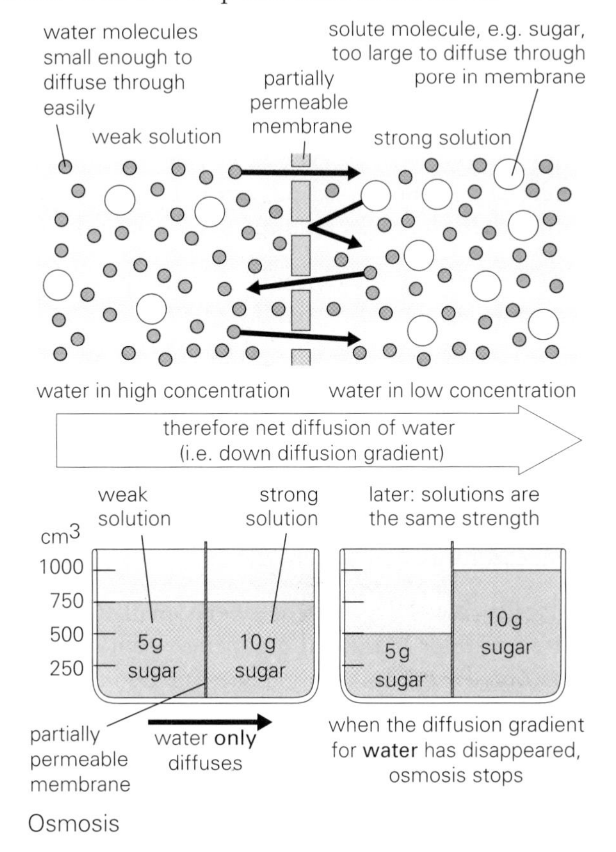

Osmosis

ovary An ovary is a female sex organ. It produces female gametes called eggs or ova.

oxidation A reaction where a substance gains oxygen or loses hydrogen. For example, magnesium is oxidised when it burns in oxygen.

$$2Mg(s) + O_2(g) \rightarrow 2MgO(s)$$

Hydrogen chloride is oxidised when it is converted to chlorine.

$$MnO_2(s) + 4HCl(g) \rightarrow MnCl_2(aq) + 2H_2O(l) + Cl_2(g)$$

A more advanced definition of oxidation is a process where electrons are lost. For example, at the positive electrode in electrolysis, e.g. $2Cl^- \rightarrow Cl_2 + 2^{e-}$

The opposite of oxidation is reduction.

oxide Compound of an element with oxygen. A basic oxide is an oxide of a metal. A neutral oxide, e.g. carbon monoxide, has no reaction with acids or alkalis and has a pH of 7. Acidic oxides are non-metal oxides which react with alkalis to form a salt and water. An amphoteric oxide, e.g. aluminium oxide, can act as an acidic oxide or a basic oxide, depending upon conditions.

oxidise (See **oxidation**.)

oxidising agent An oxidising agent, e.g. chlorine, oxidises another substance. Common oxidising agents include oxygen, chlorine, iodine, concentrated sulphuric acid, concentrated nitric acid and potassium manganate(VII).

oxygen debt A situation can arise where a muscle cell can no longer respire aerobically and has to continue to respire, but anaerobically. The lactic acid produced during the period of enforced anaerobic respiration is oxidised later. The oxygen required – the oxygen debt, is 'paid back' by a continued and raised breathing rate, well after the exercise has finished.

pancreas The pancreas is a gland that produces digestive enzymes and hormones.

Pangea A supercontinent which expanded to produce the present continents.

parallel A circuit or part of a circuit where there is more than one current path.

parasite An organism that lives in or on another living organism (host) from which it gains nutrients, at its host's expense, is called a parasite, e.g. tapeworm, mistletoe.

pathogen Pathogens are microscopic organisms that cause disease. They include some bacteria, some fungi, all viruses and some protozoa (single celled animals).

penicillin (See **antibiotic**.)

perennating organ Perennial plants can live for several years. They produce perennating organs which allow them to overwinter, e.g. bulb, corm, tuber.

period A horizontal row in the Periodic Table (see p. 76).

peristalsis Movements caused by alternate, antagonistic contractions of circular and longitudinal muscles in the walls of tubes produce peristaltic waves, e.g. gut movements. Circular muscle contraction makes the cross-section of the tube smaller. Material is squeezed along a tube much in the same way that toothpaste is squeezed out of its tube.

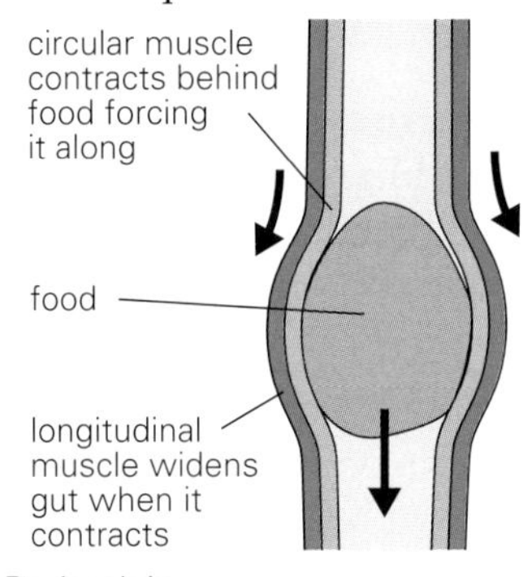

Peristalsis

permanent hardness This hardness of water is caused by dissolved calcium sulphate and magnesium sulphate. It is not removed by boiling.

petrification The process of fossilisation, where minerals are laid down over a long period of time in the tissues of a dead organism 'turning it to stone', is called petrification.

petrol A low boiling point fraction produced from fractional distillation of crude oil.

petroleum (See **crude oil**.)

petroleum gas (or **natural gas**) Gas found with petroleum made up largely of methane.

pH A scale measuring acidity and alkalinity. A pH value of 7 is exactly neutral. Values below 7 are acids, with the lower the value the stronger the acid. Values greater than 7 are alkaline with the higher the value the stronger the alkali. The pH value can be found with Universal indicator or with a pH meter.

phagocyte (See **phagocytosis**.)

phagocytosis Phagocytosis is the feeding process that is typical of phagocytes. They engulf material so forming a food vacuole. Some types of white blood cells are phagocytes. They engulf bacteria.

phenotype The phenotype of a particular gene describes the way the physical and physiological features of the characteristic are shown.

phloem Plants transport organic compounds in a tissue known as phloem.

phosphorus A solid non-metallic element. Phosphorus is an element required for good plant growth.

photosynthesis Photosynthesis is the process by which green plants manufacture glucose from inorganic raw materials. They absorb water from the soil and use respiratory and atmospheric carbon dioxide as a source of carbon. The process is dependent on light and only occurs in those cells that have chlorophyll.

$$\text{carbon dioxide} + \text{water} \xrightarrow[\text{light energy}]{\text{chlorophyll absorbs}} \text{glucose} + \text{oxygen}$$

The light energy absorbed by chlorophyll is used to split water molecules to produce oxygen and the capacity to reduce carbon dioxide. At the same time some ATP is made which is used to power the synthetic process. This photo-reduction of carbon dioxide provides the plant with glucose, which it then uses as the starting point for the synthesis of other organic compounds.

phototropism Phototropism is a plant growth response to light. Shoots are positively phototropic and roots are negatively phototropic.

pitch How high or low a sound appears to be. The pitch of a sound is related to its frequency. The higher the frequency of a sound, the higher the pitch.

placenta The placenta is a structure formed in the pregnant uterus from part of the lining of the uterus and embryonic membranes. It provides an exchange surface between the embryo and its mother. Nutrients, oxygen and wastes are exchanged along concentration gradients that exist between the separated, fetal and maternal blood systems.

planet A planet is a large body that orbits a star.

plates Huge sections of the Earth's crust which float on the mantle.

pole In magnetism, the strongest part of a magnet. The pole of a magnet that points towards magnetic North is called its North-seeking pole and that that points towards magnetic South is called the South-seeking pole. In electricity, the term pole is used to refer to a terminal of a cell or battery.

pollen Pollen grains are produced in the stamens of flowering plants. A mature, germinating pollen grain contains three nuclei. These are the pollen tube nucleus and two nuclei that function as male gametes. The pollen grain is a spore acting as a vehicle to transport male gametes to the female structure.

polyester A condensation polymer produced by reactions of molecules containing –OH and –COOH groups.

polymer A long chain molecule built up of a large number of small units, called monomers, joined together by a process called polymerisation.

polysaccharide A polysaccharide is a condensation polymer produced by a series of condensation reactions with a monosaccharide, such as glucose, as the monomer. Examples are starch, pectin and cellulose.

positive The pole of a cell or battery that attracts negative charges and repels positive charges.

potassium A reactive alkali metal in group 1 of the Periodic Table (see p. 76). Potassium is an element required for good plant growth.

potential difference There is a potential difference between two points if a current passes between them when they are connected by a conductor. Potential difference is commonly referred to as voltage.

power Power is the rate of working or energy transfer. It is measured in watts (W). One watt is equivalent to a rate of working of 1 J/s.

precipitate An insoluble substance formed in a chemical reaction involving solutions.

precipitation A reaction where a precipitate is formed.

predator A predator is a carnivore which kills and eats other animals.

pressure In solids, pressure is a measure of the effect that a force has in cutting or piercing. It is calculated using *pressure = force ÷ area*. The unit of pressure is the pascal (Pa), where 1 Pa = 1 N/m^2. In liquids and gases, pressure is exerted on the walls of the container due to the collisions with the particles of the liquid or gas.

prey An animal which forms the food of a predator is called its prey.

primary In light, a primary colour is one that cannot be produced by mixing lights of other colours. The primary colours are red, blue and green. In a transformer, the primary coil is the input coil.

prism In optics, a prism is a triangular-shaped block of glass or perspex. Prisms are used to disperse light into its constituent colours and to change the path of light using total internal reflection.

producer An organism that produces organic compounds (food) from inorganic raw materials is called a producer. Green plants are producers.

Prokaryotae Prokaryotae is a classification group (Kingdom). It is the group that includes bacteria.

proportional Two physical quantities are proportional if doubling the value of one quantity causes the value of the other quantity to double. An example is the relationship between current and voltage for a fixed resistor.

protein A natural condensation polymer produced by linking together amino acids.

Protoctista Protoctista is the classification group (Kingdom) which includes algae and protozoa (single-celled animals).

proton A proton is an atomic particle found in the nucleus. It is similar in mass to the neutron but has a positive charge.

protoplasm Protoplasm includes the chemical components of living material.

protoplasm = cytoplasm + nucleus

protozoa (See **pathogen**.)

pulmonary circuit The blood vessels which take blood from the heart to the lungs and back to the heart form the pulmonary circuit.

pure substance A single substance that contains nothing apart from the substance itself. Pure substances have definite melting and boiling points.

pyramid of number and biomass The numbers of individuals or the total biomass at each trophic level of a food chain can be graphed. The results produce a pyramid-shaped graph.

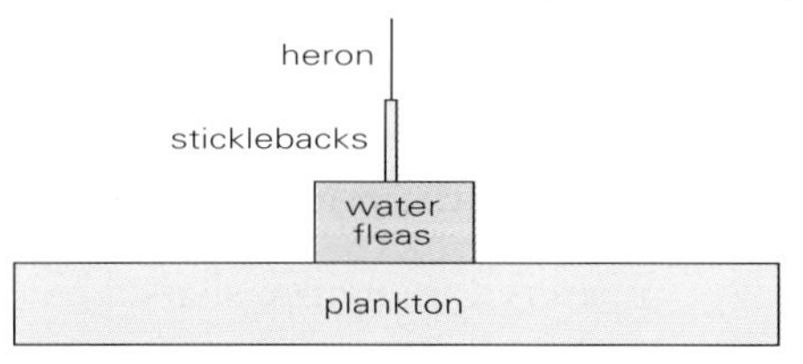

Pyramid of numbers for a freshwater food chain

qualitative A qualitative study is one which depends upon changes in appearance only.

quantitative A quantitative study involves studies of quantities, e.g. mass, volume, etc.

radiation In radioactivity, radiation is emitted when an unstable nucleus changes to a more stable form. The term radiation is also used to describe any electromagnetic wave given out by an object.

radio waves The part of the electromagnetic spectrum with the longest wavelength. Radio waves are used to transmit information from one part of the Earth to another.

radioactive A radioactive substance has unstable nuclei. Radiation is emitted when an unstable nucleus decays to a more stable form.

radiocarbon dating A method of estimating the age of dead biological material by comparing the amount of the radioactive isotope carbon-14 present in the dead material with that present in living material.

random motion A motion that is neither ordered nor predictable in speed or direction. The term is used to describe the motion of the particles in a gas or liquid.

random movement Particles are moving with no pattern in their motion.

rarefaction A rarefaction forms part of a longitudinal wave where the particles of material that transmit the wave are further apart than the equilibrium separation.

reactants The substances which react together to form products.

reaction time The time that elapses between an event occurring and a person responding to that event. The distance that a vehicle travels during a driver's reaction time is called the 'thinking distance'.

reactivity series A list of metals in order of reactivity with the most reactive metal at the top of the list.

real image A real image is one that can be displayed on a screen, for example the image on the film in a camera. Light converges at a real image.

recessive A recessive allele works only when it is partnered by another like itself except for some X-linked recessives. These are single – there being no functional allele on the Y-chromosome.

red giant A red giant is a star that has gone through its main sequence, expanded and cooled.

redox reaction A reaction where both oxidation and reduction are taking place.

reducing agent Substance which brings about the reduction of another substance. Common reducing agents are metals, hydrogen and carbon monoxide.

reduction A reduction reaction is a reaction where oxygen is lost or hydrogen is gained. For example, lead(II) oxide is converted to lead by heating a mixture of lead(II) oxide and carbon. Lead(II) oxide is reduced to lead.

$PbO + C \rightarrow Pb + CO$

Ammonia burns in oxygen to produce nitrogen

$4NH_3 + 3O_2 \rightarrow 2N_2 + 6H_2O$

Ammonia is oxidised to nitrogen. A more advanced definition of reduction is a process where electrons are gained, e.g. copper ions deposited at the cathode during electrolysis.

$Cu^{2+} + 2e- \rightarrow Cu$

reflection The change in direction when light or other wave motion rebounds at a boundary between two materials.

refraction The change in speed when light or other wave motion passes from one material into another. The change in speed causes a change in wavelength and may cause a change in direction.

renewable A renewable energy source is one that will not become exhausted within the lifetime of the Earth, e.g. wind.

replication Replication is the process that provides an exact copy of DNA and therefore a duplicate set of chromosomes prior to cell division.

reproduction Cells or organisms increase in number by a process known as reproduction. Cell reproduction occurs by mitosis. Organisms reproduce asexually or sexually, some by both methods.

repulsion A force where two objects push away from each other. The forces between the objects are equal in size and opposite in direction.

resistance A measure of the opposition that a conductor has to electric current passing in it. Resistance is defined as *voltage ÷ current* and is measured in ohms (Ω).

resistor A circuit component that has resistance.

resonance A large amplitude vibration that occurs when an object is forced to vibrate at its natural frequency of vibration.

respiration Respiration is the process whereby energy is released from food molecules and made available for cells to do biological work. Part of the process goes on in the cytoplasm. Most of the energy is released by enzymes that operate inside mitochondria. The energy released is stored in adenosine triphosphate. (See also **aerobic** and **anaerobic respiration**.)

retina The retina is the lining at the back of the eye. It includes two types of light-sensitive cells: rods and cones. Rods are sensitive to low light intensity but allow black and white vision only. The cones provide colour vision and detail but only in bright light. The cones are concentrated in the fovea, which lies on the optical axis of the eye. The rods are distributed throughout the rest of the retina.

reversible reaction A reaction which can go forwards or backwards depending upon conditions. In an enclosed system an equilibrium can be set up.

ribosome Ribosomes are cell organelles. Some are attached to membranes, others are free within the cytoplasm of a cell. They are the site where proteins are made.

rock cycle A cycle showing how new rocks are formed and old rocks are returned to the magma for re-use.

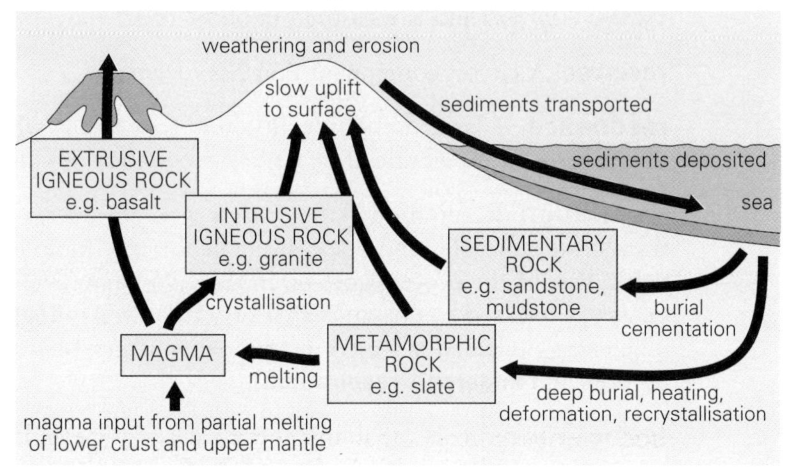

The rock cycle

rusting An oxidation process of iron and steel. Iron and steel rust in the presence of oxygen (air) and water. Rust is hydrated iron(III) oxide. The process can be summarised by the ionic equation

$Fe \rightarrow Fe^{3+} + 3^{e-}$.

saliva Saliva is a digestive juice produced by salivary glands in the mouth. It contains the enzyme amylase.

$$\text{starch (polysaccharide)} \xrightarrow{\text{amylase}} \text{maltose (disaccharide)}$$

salt A substance which is formed as a product of neutralisation.

saponification Splitting up of esters in natural fats and oils by hydrolysis using boiling alkali. The products are soap and glycerol.

saprophyte A saprophyte is an organism, e.g. fungus, that obtains nutrients from dead organic material. Saprophytes release hydrolytic enzymes onto the food material which is digested and absorbed. (See also **hydrolysis**.)

satellite An object that orbits a planet. Moons are natural satellites. Artificial satellites are used in telecommunications, for monitoring the weather, navigation and surveillance.

saturated compound A compound which contains only single covalent bonds, e.g. ethane C_2H_6. An unsaturated compound contains one or more double or triple bonds.

saturated solution A solution in which no more solute will dissolve providing temperature remains constant.

secondary A secondary colour is one that can be produced by mixing light of two primary colours. The secondary colours are yellow, cyan and magenta. In a transformer, the secondary coil is the output coil.

sedimentary Rocks that are composed of compacted fragments of older rocks which have been eroded, transported and deposited in layers of the floor of a lake or sea, e.g. sandstone.

selective breeding Artificial selection is used by Man in selective breeding to develop improved breeds of wheat, cattle, roses, etc.

selective reabsorption Selective reabsorption is the process which allows some substances, filtered from the blood in the kidney, to be removed from the urine before it leaves the kidney tubules. In this way, glucose and some of the water and salts are retained.

selective weedkiller A selective weedkiller is a chemical used to kill some plants and not others.

selectively permeable membrane A selectively permeable membrane allows some particles to pass through it and not others.

series A circuit where there is only one current path. In a series circuit, the current passing through each component has the same value.

sexual reproduction Sexual reproduction increases the number of individuals by a process that involves the fusion of the nuclei (fertilisation) of two, different, gametes. This contrasts with asexual reproduction where new individuals are formed from pieces of parent tissue with an established genotype.

shale A sedimentary rock made up of very fine mud or clay particles compressed to form the rock.

shell Electrons are around the nucleus in shells or energy levels. Each shell can hold a maximum number of electrons.

silicon(IV) oxide The chief chemical constituent of sand.

silver chloride A white insoluble silver compound precipitated when a solution containing chloride ions is added to silver nitrate solution.

skeleton Skeletons fall into one of three main groups: hydrostatic (fluid provides the skeleton), exoskeletons and endoskeletons. All three carry out similar functions. They support the organism, maintain its shape, protect the internal structures from damage and enable movement.

sodium carbonate Hydrated sodium carbonate is called washing soda. It has a formula $Na_2CO_3 \cdot 10H_2O$. It is a cheap alkali and water softener.

sodium chloride The chemical name for common salt, NaCl.

sodium hydrogencarbonate This is sometimes called bicarbonate of soda and is a weak alkali. It has a chemical formula $NaHCO_3$.

sodium hydroxide A cheap alkali produced by the electrolysis of brine.

solar system A star and all the objects that orbit it.

solenoid A coil of wire, with or without a core, used as an electromagnet.

solubility The number of grams of a solid solute dissolving in 100 g of solvent at a particular temperature. For most solutes the solubility rises with rise in temperature. The solubility of sodium chloride is approximately the same at all temperatures. For gases, the solubility decreases with rising temperature.

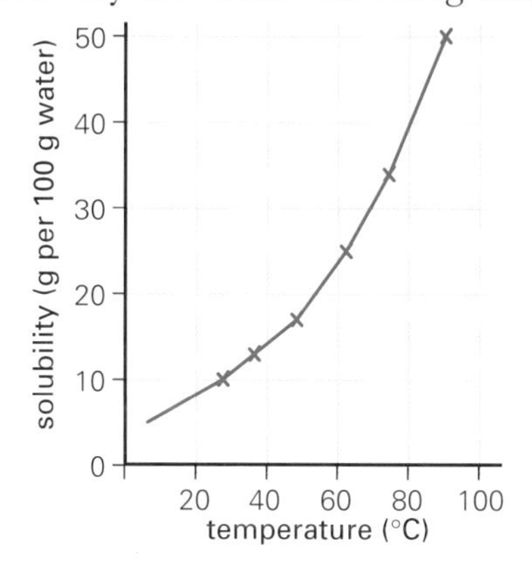

Solubility curve of potassium chlorate in water

solution The mixture formed when a solute dissolves in a solvent.

solution mining Salt can be mined by drilling a hole down to the salt deposits and pumping water down the hole. The salt dissolves and the salt solution (or brine) can be pumped back to the surface. This is called solution mining.

sound A longitudinal wave motion with a frequency in the range 20 Hz to 20 000 Hz. (See also **ultrasound**.)

species All the members of a single species have similar characteristics. They can interbreed and produce fertile offspring.

spectrum A family of waves with a range of frequencies and wavelengths.

speed How fast an object travels, calculated using *average speed = distance travelled ÷ time taken*. Speed is measured in m/s.

sperm A sperm is a motile, male sex cell. It carries one complete set of single chromosomes – the paternal chromosomes.

star An astronomical object that generates energy due to nuclear fusion. A star gives out light and/or other forms of electromagnetic radiation.

starch A natural condensation polymer with glucose monomer units. Starch forms a blue-black colour with iodine solution. Acid hydrolysis of starch produces glucose. Enzyme hydrolysis with enzymes in saliva produces a disaccharide called maltose.

static electricity An unbalanced charge that is not moving is called static electricity. A common cause of static electricity is the transfer of electrons when two objects are rubbed together. The object that gains electrons becomes charged negatively while the object that loses electrons becomes charged positively.

stimulus A stimulus is a change in the environment which is registered and initiates a response. Light, sound and a smell are examples of stimuli.

stomata The surface of a leaf is continuous in order to conserve water. Respiratory and photosynthetic gaseous exchange must however take place. The leaf surface is perforated by stomata enabling this exchange to occur. A single stoma is a pore bordered by a pair of guard cells. The guard cells show unequally thickened walls – those walls bordering the pore are thicker. Consequently, osmotic changes that occur in the guard cells cause the cells to change shape. When the guard cells are inflated the pore is opened. When they lose water, the guard cells close the pore.

stopping distance The total distance that a vehicle travels between when the driver notices a hazard and when the vehicle stops. It is made up of 'thinking distance' and 'braking distance'.

substrate A substance on which an enzyme can act.

sulphuric acid Sulphuric acid, H_2SO_4, is the acid produced by the Contact process. Salts made from it are called sulphates.

Sun The Earth's star.

supernova A supernova is a star at the end of its main sequence. It glows very brightly as it collapses due to gravitational forces.

survival of the fittest Variation exists in sexually produced offspring. Some variants have an advantage over others, so they survive.

switch A device for making and breaking a circuit by closing or separating a pair of contacts.

symbiosis Symbiosis is a feeding relationship where an organism of one species lives in or on another organism of a different species with both partners benefiting, e.g. nitrogen-fixing bacteria and legumes.

synapse Nerve impulses may pass along a series of neurones in a nerve pathway. A microscopic gap exists between two consecutive neurones. The gap, e.g. between the terminal dendrites of one neurone and the receptive dendrites of the next, is called a synapse. Information is relayed across the synapse by the diffusion of neurotransmitter substances.

synovial joint A synovial joint is capsular, membrane-lined and lubricated by synovial fluid.

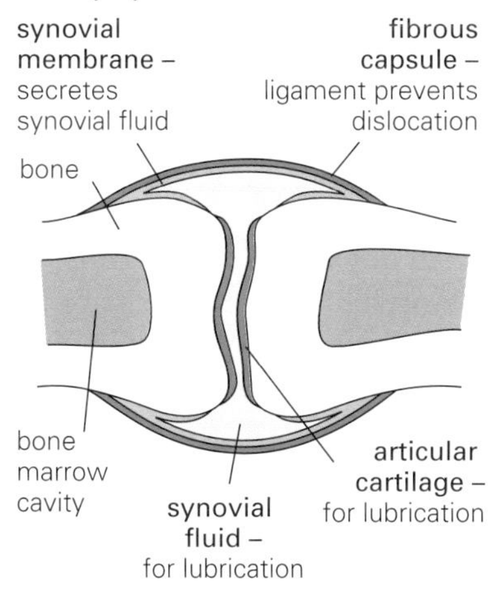

A synovial joint

synthesis The formation of a compound from its constituent elements, e.g. iron(II) sulphide from iron and sulphur. (See also **combination**.)

synthetic polymers Synthetic polymers are made from monomers obtained from products of crude oil.

systemic circuit The blood vessels which take blood from the heart to the various organs of the body and return it to the heart are known as the systemic circuit.

target cell Many different hormones may be in circulation in an animal at any one time. Each hormone affects particular cells. Those cells affected by a specific hormone are called its target cells. Target cells have surface membranes that can recognise specific hormones.

taxon (See **classification**.)

temperature Temperature is a measure of how hot an object is.

temporary hardness Hardness of water that can be removed by boiling. It is caused by dissolved calcium hydrogencarbonate. This decomposes on boiling to form calcium carbonate.

tendon Tendons attach muscle to bone. They are very strong and inelastic.

terminal A cell or battery has two terminals, called positive and negative. When connected in a circuit, the direction of the current in the circuit is from the positive terminal towards the negative terminal.

terminal velocity An object travels at a constant, terminal velocity when the driving force and the resistive forces are balanced, that is, equal in size and opposite in direction.

thermal energy The energy an object has due to its temperature.

thermistor The resistance of a thermistor depends on its temperature. Thermistors are of two types, ntc (negative temperature coefficient) and ptc (positive temperature coefficient). The resistance of an ntc thermistor decreases as its temperature increases.

thermit reaction The thermit reaction is a displacement reaction where iron is obtained from iron(III) oxide using aluminium powder. This is an exothermic reaction.

thermoplastic polymers Polymers which melt on heating without decomposing. On cooling the melt hardens to reform the original polymer.

thermosetting polymers Polymers which do not melt on heating but decompose. They do not re-form the original polymer on cooling. An example of a thermosetting polymer is Bakelite.

thorax The human thorax is that part of the body that contains the heart and lungs – the chest. It is separated from the abdomen by the diaphragm.

thyroid The thyroid gland is a hormonal gland that secretes the hormone thyroxine. This hormone controls rate of growth.

tissue A tissue is a group of cells of the same type having a specific function.

tissue fluid Tissue fluid is plasma which leaks from capillaries. The fluid and blood proteins are returned to the blood via the lymphatic system.

total internal reflection This may occur when light meets a boundary between two materials and the speed of light in the material that it is travelling in is less than the speed of light in the material beyond the boundary. If the angle of incidence at the boundary is greater than the critical angle all the light is reflected; this is known as total internal reflection. Total internal reflection is used in reflecting prisms to turn light through 90° or 180°, and in fibre optics.

toxin A toxin is a poisonous protein produced, e.g., by a pathogen.

transformer A transformer is an electromagnetic device that changes the size of an alternating voltage. It consists of two coils of wire wrapped on an iron core. An alternating voltage applied to the input, or primary coil, causes an alternating voltage to be induced in the output, or secondary coil. The ratio of the primary and secondary voltages is equal to the ratio of the number of turns on the coils:

$$\frac{\text{primary voltage}}{\text{secondary voltage}} = \frac{\text{number of primary turns}}{\text{number of secondary turns}}$$

transition metal The block of metals between the two parts of the main block in the Periodic Table (see p. 76). Transition metals are usually dense metals that are much less reactive than alkali metals.

transpiration Water evaporates from a plant shoot system, in particular through the stomata of leaves. This loss of water is called transpiration. Transpiration lowers the water content of the spongy mesophyll cells. Water leaves the xylem supplying the mesophyll to restore the balance. Water moves up the xylem from the root system. Water enters the root system by osmosis. The continuous flow of water through the xylem of a plant is called the transpiration stream. The rate of transpiration is affected by several environmental factors. Any factor that increases the rate of evaporation of water will increase the rate of transpiration. An increase in air temperature, air movement or a decrease in relative humidity will increase evaporation and therefore transpiration also. Reduced uptake by the roots or excessive loss by transpiration may result in closure of the stomata and conservation of water. Prolonged water imbalance may lead to wilting and possible death.

transportation One of the steps in the formation of sedimentary rocks.

transverse A wave motion in which the oscillations are at right angles to the direction of wave travel is a transverse wave. Light and other forms of electromagnetic radiation travel as transverse waves.

trend A pattern in properties.

triceps The triceps is the extensor muscle that operates at the elbow joint.

trophic level The trophic level of an organism describes its level of feeding in a food chain, e.g. producers will be at level 1.

tropism A tropism is a plant growth response where the direction of the response is related to the direction of the stimulus, e.g. phototropism and geotropism.

troposphere The lowest layer of the Earth's atmosphere. All weather processes take place in the troposphere.

turbine In the generation of electricity, a turbine is a device that transfers energy from a moving fluid to a generator. In hydroelectric power stations the turbines are water-driven. Steam turbines are used in coal-fired power stations.

turgor Water may enter a plant cell until the vacuole is full and the cytoplasm pushed out against the cell wall. When the cell wall is fully stretched it becomes rigid and will prevent the entry of any more water. Such a cell is said to be turgid or showing full turgor. This hydrostatic pressure that inflates a cell is important in the support of plants, particularly those with little xylem.

ultrafiltration One example of ultrafiltration is the separation of molecules and ions from blood in the kidney leading to the formation of urine.

ultrasound A longitudinal wave with a frequency above the range of human hearing. Ultrasound is used for echo-sounding and scanning body tissue.

ultraviolet Electromagnetic radiation that has a wavelength shorter than that of light but longer than that of X-rays and gamma rays. Exposure to ultraviolet radiation can cause sunburn and skin cancer.

unicellular A unicellular organism is composed of one cell only.

universal indicator A mixture of indicators used for finding the pH of a substance.

universe Everything that exists.

urine Urine is the solution in which urea and other nitrogenous waste products leave the body of a terrestrial mammal accompanied by water, sodium and other inorganic ions.

uterus The uterus is part of the mammalian female reproductive organs. It is a muscular structure that accommodates the developing fetus during pregnancy. Contractions of the smooth muscle in its wall are responsible for the birth of the baby.

vaccine A vaccine is a preparation containing antigens given to a patient in order to initiate an immune response. This gives the person protection in the event of a future infection thanks to the memory cells that will be present as a result of the vaccination. The memory cells can make antibodies rapidly to destroy the invading antigens.

vacuole Vacuoles are intra-cellular spaces in the cytoplasm. They are spaces enclosed within membranes. The membranes are selectively permeable exercising some control over what can get in and/or out of the vacuole. They are more obvious in plant cells than animal cells. In plants they have a significant role in the support of non-woody tissue and whole organisms. Vacuoles may serve as storage areas.

vacuum A vacuum is a region of space that contains nothing. It is not possible to create a total vacuum on Earth, so the term is often used to refer to a region where the pressure is less than atmospheric pressure.

variable resistor The resistance of a variable resistor can be changed mechanically, by moving a slider along a piece of wire or carbon track.

variation Variation is expressed in the differences that are shown between the offspring of sexually reproducing organisms. Variation arises in part due to the meiotic divisions associated with the production of gametes.

vasoconstriction and vasodilation These terms are applied to changes shown by arterioles in the skin. The relative volume of blood allowed to flow near to the surface of a mammal, in the skin capillaries, affects the amount of heat lost from it. If less blood flows, less heat will be lost and vice versa. The term vasodilation is used to describe the condition where the muscles in the walls of the arterioles are relaxed and dilated by the blood flowing through them. Vasoconstriction is the term used to describe the converse. Vasodilation and vasoconstriction are involved in the regulation of body temperature.

vegetative reproduction This term is used to describe asexual reproduction in plants and includes techniques such as taking leaf or stem cuttings, budding, grafting and layering.

velocity The velocity of a moving object describes both its speed and direction. Velocity can have both positive and negative values, indicating movement in opposite directions.

ventricle There are two ventricles in the human heart. They are very muscular. The right ventricle pumps blood to the lungs and back to the heart. Muscle contractions in the wall of the left ventricle are strong enough to pump blood out to the rest of the body and get it back to the heart too.

vertebrates Animals that have a vertebral column (backbone) are called vertebrates. Fish, amphibians, reptiles, birds and mammals are all vertebrates.

vibration An alternative word for oscillation, a vibration describes a to-and-fro motion.

virtual image An image that does not exist and cannot be displayed on a screen. Light does not pass through a virtual image. An example is the image in a plane mirror.

virus Viruses are extremely small, lying within the range 10^{-8} m to 10^{-7} m. They all have a central core containing a nucleic acid. The nucleic acid is surrounded by a protein case – the capsid. Viruses cannot carry out respiration, irritability, nutrition, movement and excretion – processes normally associated with living things. They can reproduce, but only after they have entered a living host cell. All viruses behave as obligate parasites.

viscosity A measure of the ease with which a liquid can be poured. A liquid with a high viscosity, e.g. treacle, is difficult to pour.

vitamin Vitamins are essential components of a healthy diet.

volt The unit of voltage or potential difference.

voltage An everyday term used in place of potential difference. There is a voltage between two points if a current passes when they are connected by a conductor.

voltmeter An instrument used to measure voltage or potential difference. A voltmeter is always connected in parallel with a component in a circuit to measure the voltage across it.

volume The amount of space occupied by an object. Volume is measured in cm^3 or m^3.

water of crystallisation Water which forms part of the structure in a crystal, e.g. $CuSO_4 \cdot 5H_2O$.

water potential Water potential is a measure of the tendency for water to move away from a particular place. Pure water has the maximum water potential – adding solutes lowers the water potential.

watt The watt is the unit of power. One watt (1 W) is equal to an energy transfer at the rate of one joule per second (1 J/s).

wave A wave transmits energy through space by means of a repetitive oscillation. Waves can be longitudinal or transverse.

wavelength The length of one complete cycle of a wave motion.

weathering The action of wind, rain, snow, etc on rocks. These changes can be physical or chemical.

weight The gravitational force that pulls an object towards the centre of the planet that it is on. On the surface of the Earth, each kilogramme of mass has a weight of 9.8 N.

white dwarf A white dwarf is a star that is created when a red giant contracts due to gravitational forces. In a white dwarf, fusion of helium nuclei causes the formation of carbon and oxygen nuclei and releases energy.

whole preservation Whole preservation is a process of fossilisation where a plant or an animal has been preserved intact (including gut content in some animals).

work Work is done when a force causes motion. An energy transfer always takes place when work is done. The work done and energy transfer are both measured in joules (J).

X- and Y-chromosomes These are the sex-chromosomes. A woman has two X-chromosomes, XX, in the nuclei of her body cells. A man has one of each, XY. Human eggs have an X-chromosome. Half a man's sperms have an X-chromosome and half have a Y-chromosome.

X-ray Very short wavelength electromagnetic waves that are very penetrative. They are distinguished from gamma rays only in their origin; X-rays are produced in X-ray tubes. The partial absorption of X-rays by bone makes them useful in taking X-ray photographs.

xylem Plant tissue used in the conduction of water.

zinc A dull soft, silvery metal often used in alloys such as brass.

zygote The cell formed by the fusion of two gametes is called a zygote. The zygotic nucleus will be diploid. A zygote undergoes cell division and differentiation to form an embryo.

zymase An enzyme in yeast which acts on sugar solution to produce ethanol by fermentation.

Periodic Table

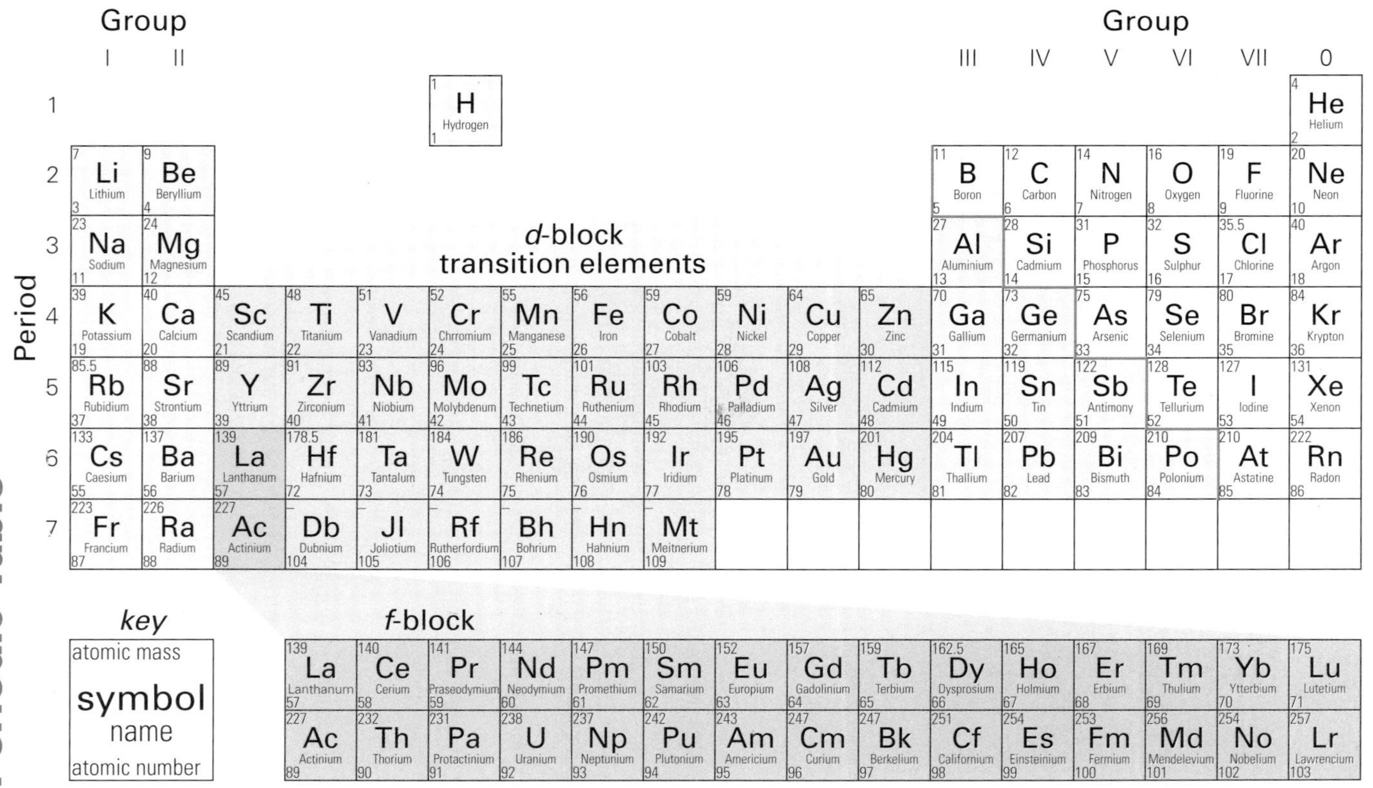